The last hundred and fifty years have seen technological strides unmatched in any other era in the history of man—but this book is concerned with technical matters only where they are essential to the argument. It assumes that machines are less important than what men do with them—or what they do with men.

One group of pieces brings home the realities of space flight by considering what the tourists of the 21st century will meet when vacationing on the Moon, on Mars, or at a satellite hotel—possibilities much closer than jet-powered economy flights would have seemed a lifetime ago.

"Report on Planet Three" provides a lively understanding of our own world as seen through the somewhat jaundiced eye of a Martian observer, while "where's Everybody?" deals with the curious fact that Earth has never had any visitors from space.

But Mr. Clarke's imagination is not content with soaring out to the stars. In "Of Mind and Matter" he considers the effect of recent electronic research on such problems as the identity of the individual and survival after death.

Through all of his writing runs the thread of reality, woven so strongly into the construction of his theories that no one can doubt that Mr. Clarke is much more than his modest claim of "minor prophet." Reading these articles is not only fun—it is a startling glimpse into the future of all our lives.

ARTHUR C. CLARKE

THE CHALLENGE
* OF THE *
* *
SPACESHIP
*

BALLANTINE BOOKS
NEW YORK

First Ballantine Books edition, 1961

Published in co-operation with Harper and Brothers.

Grateful acknowledgment is made to the following magazines in which these articles first appeared: *Coronet, Fantasy and Science Fiction, Harper's Magazine, Holiday, Horizon, Journal of the British Interplanetary Society, The Saturday Review,* and *The Times Magazine.*

Library of Congress catalog card number: 59-8248

BALLANTINE BOOKS, INC.
101 Fifth Avenue, New York 3, N. Y.

CONTENTS

To Carl Biemiller and Harry Sions,
Chief Instigators of the ensuing pages

★

★ THE main theme of this book is the impact of the coming Space Age upon our hitherto Earth-bound species. Looking past the immediate present, and ignoring both the occasional triumphs and more frequent failures of today's satellites and rocket probes, it attempts to view the conquest of space as part of a historical process. Except where they are essential to the argument, it is not in the least concerned with technical matters; it assumes that machines are less important than what men do with them—or what they do with men.

Though the various examinations of the Man-Space relationship that follow look at the subject from different angles, some overlapping is inevitable and some is deliberate. I have tried to edit out all unnecessary repetition, but when a thing is really important, it is worth saying more than once.

Interleaved among these philosophical and cultural speculations are examples of straight science reporting, most of them from the pages of *Holiday* Magazine. Sometimes, as in the trio of pieces giving helpful advice to interplanetary tourists, the reporting is not so straight. However, anyone who reads this book as a whole will be in little danger of confusing fact with fiction.

If you will excuse the modest cough of the minor prophet, I would like to draw attention to some points where reality has agreed with my predictions in the interval since the first appearance of this book. *The Men on the Moon* was published only a few months before Lunik III made its flight, and though I doubt if *Holiday* Magazine has a wide circulation in the U.S.S.R., almost all my suggestions for naming the craters on the other side of the Moon have been adopted.

In particular, Tsiolkovsky has one of the most splendid of all lunar formations, which he well deserves. I am also pleased to note that Jules Verne has become the second science-fiction writer to be immortalized on the Moon. (The first? Johannes Kepler.)

At the end of *The Radio Universe,* I remarked that some radio astronomers must cherish the secret hope that they can detect intelligently-produced signals from space. That hope is no longer a secret; the first attempt to do this—Project Ozma—was made during 1960. No one expected success at the first try, with the very small antenna system employed, nor was it obtained. But the experiment will be repeated with far larger instruments, on Earth and in space—and especially on the far side of the Moon, where they will be shielded from the roar and crackle of man-made interference. One day, it will succeed: there will be someone at the other end of the line and the question I ask in the chapter "Where's Everybody?" will be answered at last.

Colombo, May 1961.

★ THE CHALLENGE OF THE SPACESHIP*
★

★ A HISTORIAN of the twenty-first century, looking back past our own age to the beginnings of human civilization, will be conscious of four great turning points which mark the end of one era and the dawn of a new and totally different mode of life. Two of these events are lost, probably forever, in the primeval night before history began. The invention of agriculture led to the founding of settled communities and gave Man the leisure and social intercourse without which progress is impossible. The taming of fire made him virtually independent of climate and, most important of all, led to the working of metals and so set him upon the road of technological development—that road which was to lead, centuries later, to the steam engine, the Industrial Revolution, and the age of steel and gasoline and surface transportation through which we are now passing.

The third revolution began, as all the world knows, in a squash court in Chicago on December 2, 1942, when the first self-sustaining nuclear reaction was started by Man. We are still too close to that cataclysmic event to see it in its true perspective, but we know that it will change our world, for better or for worse, almost beyond recognition. And we know too that it is linked with the fourth and in some ways greatest change of all—the crossing of space and the exploration

* "The Challenge of the Spaceship" is a much revised and updated version of a talk delivered to the British Interplanetary Society in 1946, during my first term as chairman. Despite the obvious derivation of the title, it should not be assumed that I now owe any particular allegiance to Professor Toynbee, though at the time of writing I was much taken by a lecture I had just heard him deliver on "The Unification of the World."

One other historical note: I am still rather proud of the fact that when I sent the first printed version of this paper to George Bernard Shaw (then in his ninety-first year), he promptly joined the British Interplanetary Society, and remained a member until his death.

of the other planets. For though the first space vehicles were chemically fueled, only atomic energy is adequate to lift really large pay loads out of the Earth's gravitational field— that invisible maelstrom whose tug can still be felt a million miles away.

Prophecy is a dangerous and thankless business, frequently fatal to those who practice it. We have, however, learned from past experience that even the most extravagant forecast seldom overtakes the truth. H. G. Wells once wrote—and was no doubt laughed to scorn for his folly—that the airplane *might* have some influence upon warfare by the year 1950. He never dared to imagine that by that date aircraft would not only have become of supreme importance but would have been challenged by still newer weapons.

It is certainly not being rash—it may indeed be conservative—to assume that by the last quarter of this century an efficient and reliable method of nuclear propulsion for space vehicles will have been perfected. Atomic power is hardly likely to advance the conquest of space by more than ten years, but it may make it practical almost from the beginning. It would mean that the whole Solar System, and not merely the Moon, would be immediately accessible to Man. As our first space probes have demonstrated, it requires very little more power to reach the planets than it does to go to the Moon, but the most economical voyages involve months or even years of free coasting along orbits curving halfway round the Sun. With atomic power these journeys could be cut to a fraction of the time. For example, the "cheapest" journey to Mars—as far as fuel is concerned—lasts 258 days. With a nuclear-propelled ship, traveling by a more direct route at quite a moderate speed, it need take only a few weeks.

There are still some scientists who consider that there is no point in sending men into space, even when it becomes technically possible; machines, they argue, can do all that is necessary. Such an outlook is incredibly shortsighted; worse than that, it is stupid, for it completely ignores human nature. Though the specific ideal of astronautics are new, the motives and impulses underlying them are as old as the race—and, in the ultimate analysis, they owe as much to emotion as to reason. Even if we could learn nothing in space that our instruments would not already tell us, we should go there just the same.

Some men compose music or spend their lives trying to catch and hold forever the last colors of the dying day, or a pattern of clouds that, through all eternity, will never come again. Others make voyages of exploration across the world, while some make equally momentous journeys in quiet studies with no more equipment than pencil and paper. If you asked these men the purpose of their music, their painting, their exploring or their mathematics, they would probably say that they hoped to increase the beauty or the knowledge in the world. That answer would be true, and yet misleading. Very few indeed would give the simpler, more fundamental reason that they had no choice in the matter—that what they did, they did because they had to.

The urge to explore, to discover, to "follow knowledge like a sinking star," is a primary human impulse which needs, and can receive, no further justification than its own existence. The search for knowledge, said a modern Chinese philosopher, is a form of play. If this be true, then the spaceship, when it comes, will be the ultimate toy that may lead mankind from its cloistered nursery out into the playground of the stars.

However, it is not hard to think of endless and entirely valid "practical" reasons why one should wish to cross space, and some of these we will discuss later. There is no doubt that eventually sheer necessity would bring about the conquest of the other planets. It may well be impossible to have a virile, steadily advancing culture limited to a single world, and taking the long term—the very long term—view, we know that our Earth will one day become uninhabitable. The Sun is still evolving, growing steadily hotter as its central fires become banked up beneath their accumulated "ash" of helium. In the far future the oceans will boil back into the skies from which they once condensed, and life must pass from the planet Earth.

But the human race will not wait until it is kicked out. Long before the Sun's radiation has shown any measurable increase, Man will have explored all the Solar System and, like a cautious bather testing the temperature of the sea, will be making breathless little forays into the abyss that separates him from the stars.

The last quarter of this century will be an age of exploration such as Man has never before known. By the year 2000, most of the major bodies in the Solar System will probably have been reached, but it will take centuries to examine them all in any detail. Those who seem to think that the Moon is the goal of interplanetary travel should remember that the Solar System contains eight other planets, at least thirty moons and some thousands of asteroids. The total area of the major bodies is about 250 times that of Earth, though the four giant planets probably do not possess stable surfaces on which landings could be made. Nevertheless, that still leaves an area ten times as great as all the continents of Earth.

This, then, is the future which lies before us, if our civilization survives the diseases of its childhood. It is a future which some may find terrifying, as no doubt our ancestors found the hostile emptiness of the great oceans. But the men who built our world crossed those oceans and overcame those fears. If we fail before the same test, our race will have begun its slide into decadence. Remember, too, that when the great explorers of the past set sail into the unknown they said goodby for years to their homes and everything they knew. Our children will face no such loneliness. When they are among the outermost planets, when Earth is lost in the glare of the Sun and the Sun itself is no more than the brightest of the stars, they will still be able to hear its voice and to send their own words in a few hours back to the world of men.

Let us now consider the effects which interplanetary travel must have upon human institutions and ideas. The most obvious and direct result of the crossing of space will be a revolution in almost all branches of science. I will not attempt to list more than a few of the discoveries we may make when we can set up research stations and observatories upon the other planets, or in satellite orbits. One can never predict the outcome of any scientific investigation, and the greatest discoveries of all—the ones which will most influence human life—may come from sciences as yet unborn.

Astronomy and physics will, of course, be the fields of knowledge most immediately affected. In both these sciences there are whole areas where research has come to a dead end, or has never been started, because our terrestrial environment makes it impossible.

The atmosphere, which on a clear night looks so transparent, is in reality a colored filter blocking all rays beyond the ultraviolet. Even in the visible spectrum the light that finally struggles through the shifting strata above our heads is so distorted that the images it carries dance and tremble in the field of the telescope.

An observatory on the Moon, working with quite small instruments, would be many times as effective as one on Earth. Far greater magnifications could be employed, and far longer exposures used. In addition, the low gravity would make relatively simple the building of larger telescopes than have ever been constructed on this planet.

In physics and chemistry, access to vacuums of unlimited extent will open up quite new fields of investigation. The electronic scientist may well look forward to the day when he can build radio tubes miles long, if he wishes, merely by setting up his electrodes in the open! It is also interesting to speculate whether we may not learn more about gravity when we can escape partially or wholly from its influence.

Artificial satellites have already given dramatic notice of what may be achieved when we can establish permanent, manned stations in space for observation and research. Accurate weather forecasting—which, it has been estimated, would be worth five billion dollars a year to the United States alone—will probably be impossible until we can hoist the meteorologists out into space, however reluctant they may be to go there. Only from a height of several thousand miles it is possible to observe the Earth's weather pattern as a whole, and to see literally at a glance the movement of storms and rain areas.

One application of space stations and satellites, whose importance it is impossible to overestimate, is their use for communications and TV relaying. Many years ago (in the British radio magazine *Wireless World*, October, 1945) I pointed out that satellite-borne transmitters could provide interference-free reception over the whole Earth, and might indeed be the only means of establishing a global TV service.*

Should any one nation establish a satellite relay chain, it would do more than dominate the world's communications. The cultural and political impact of TV news and entertainment broadcast directly to every home on Earth would be immeasurable. When one considers the effect of TV upon ostensibly educated populations, the impact upon the semiliterate peoples of Africa and Asia may be decisive. It may well determine whether English or Russian becomes the leading world language by the end of this century.

Yet these first direct results of astronautics may be less important, in the long run, than its indirect consequences. This has proved true in the past of most great scientific achievements. Copernican astronomy, Darwin's theory of evolution, Freudian psychology—these had few immediate practical results, but their effect on human thought was tremendous.

We may expect the same of astronautics. With the expansion of the world's mental horizons may come one of the greatest outbursts of creative activity ever known. The parallel with the Renaissance, with its great flowering of the arts and sciences, is very suggestive. "In human records," wrote the anthropologist J. D. Unwin, "there is no trace of any display of productive energy which has not been preceded by a display of expansive energy. Although the two kinds of energy must be carefully distinguished, in the past they have been . . . united in the sense that one has developed out of the other." Unwin continues with this quotation from Sir James Frazer: "Intellectual progress, which reveals itself in the growth of art and science . . . receives an immense impetus from conquest and empire." Interplanetary travel is now the only form of "conquest and empire" compatible with civilization. Without it, the human mind, compelled to circle forever in its planetary goldfish bowl, must eventually stagnate.

We all know the narrow, limited type of mind which is interested in nothing beyond its town or village, and bases its judgments on those parochial standards. We are slowly—

* To the best of my knowledge, this was the first appearance of this now commonplace idea. I have since wondered, a little wistfully, if I could have patented it.

perhaps too slowly—evolving from that mentality towards a world outlook. Few things will do more to accelerate that evolution than the conquest of space. It is not easy to see how the more extreme forms of nationalism can long survive when men begin to see the Earth in its true perspective as a single small globe among the stars.

There is, of course, the possibility that as soon as space is crossed all the great powers will join in a race to claim as much territory as their ships can reach. Some American writers have even suggested that for its own protection the United States must occupy the Moon to prevent its being used as a launching site for atomic rockets. Fantastic though such remarks may seem today, they represent a danger which it would be unwise to ignore. The menace of inter-planetary imperialism can be overcome only by world-wide technical and political agreements well in advance of the actual event, and these will require continual pressure and guidance from the organizations which have studied the subject.

The Solar System is rather a large place, though whether it will be large enough for so quarrelsome an animal as *Homo sapiens* remains to be seen. But it is surely reasonable to hope that the crossing of space will have a considerable effect in reducing the psychological pressures and tensions of our present world. Much depends, of course, on the habit-ability of the other planets. It is not likely that very large populations will, at least for many centuries, be able to sub-sist outside the Earth. There may be no worlds in the Solar System upon which men can live without mechanical aids, and some of the greatest achievements of future engineering will be concerned with shaping hostile environments to human needs.

We must not, however, commit the only too common mis-take of equating mere physical expansion, or even increasing scientific knowledge, with "progress"—however that may be defined. Only little minds are impressed by sheer size and number. There would be no virtue in possessing the Universe if it brought neither wisdom nor happiness. Yet possess it we must, at least in spirit, if we are ever to answer the questions that men have asked in vain since history began.

Perhaps analogy will make my meaning clearer. Picture a small island inhabited by a race which has not yet learned the art of making ships. Looking out across the ocean this people can see many other islands, some of them much the same as its own but most of them clearly very different. From some of these islands, it is rumored, the smoke of fires has been seen ascending—though whether those fires are the work of men, no one can say.

Now these islanders are very thoughtful people, and writers of many books with such resounding titles as *The Nature of the Universe, The Meaning of Life, Mind and Reality,* and so on. Whilst admiring their enterprise, I do not think we should take their conclusions very seriously—at least until they have gone a little further afield than their own coral reef. As Robert Bridges wrote in "The Testament of Beauty":

> Wisdom will repudiate thee, if thou think to enquire WHY things are as they are or whence they came: thy task is first to learn WHAT IS . . .

That task the human race can scarcely begin to undertake while it is still earthbound.

Every thoughtful man has often asked himself: Is our race the only intelligence in the Universe, or are there other, perhaps far higher, forms of life elsewhere? There can be few questions more important than this, for upon its outcome may depend all philosophy—yes, and all religion too.

The first discovery of planets revolving round other suns, which was made in the United States in 1942, has changed all ideas of the plurality of worlds. Planets are far commoner than we had ever believed: there may be thousands of millions in this Galaxy alone. Few men today would care to argue that the Earth must be the only abode of life in the whole of space.

It is true—it is even likely—that we may encounter no other intelligence in the Solar System. That contact may have to wait for the day, perhaps ages hence, when we can reach the stars. But sooner or later it must come.

There have been many portrayals in literature of these fateful meetings. Most science-fiction writers, with characteristic lack of imagination, have used them as an excuse for stories of conflict and violence indistinguishable from those which stain the pages of our own history. Such an attitude shows a complete misunderstanding of the factors involved.

Remember the penny and the postage stamp which Sir James Jeans in *The Mysterious Universe,* balanced on Cleopatra's Needle. The obelisk represented the age of the world, the penny the whole duration of man's existence, and the stamp the length of time in which he has been slightly civilized. The period during which life will be possible on Earth corresponds to a further column of stamps hundreds of yards—perhaps a mile—in height.

Thinking of this picture, we see how infinitely improbable it is that the question of interplanetary warfare can ever arise. Any races we encounter will almost certainly be superhuman or subhuman—more likely the former, since ours must surely be one of the youngest cultures in the Universe. Only if we score a bull's-eye on that one stamp in the mile-high column will we meet a race at a level of technical development sufficiently near our own for warfare to be possible. If ships from Earth ever set out to conquer other worlds they may find themselves, at the end of their journeys, in the position of painted war canoes drawing slowly into New York Harbor.

But if the Universe does hold species so greatly in advance of our own, then why have they never visited Earth?* There is one very simple answer to this question. Let us suppose that such races exist: let us even suppose that, never having heard of Einstein, they can pass from one end of the Galaxy to the other as quickly as they wish.

That will help them less than one might think. In ten minutes, a man may walk along a beach—but in his whole lifetime he could not examine every grain of sand upon it. For all that we know, there may be fleets of survey ships diligently charting and recharting the Universe. Even making the most optimistic assumptions, they could scarcely have visited our world in the few thousand years of recorded history.

Perhaps, even at this moment, there lies in some rather extensive filing system a complete report on this planet, with

* For a more detailed discussion of this problem, and an updated version of Jeans' analogy, see "Where's Everybody?" (page 81).

maps which to us would look distorted but still recognizable. That report would show that though Earth was teeming with life, it had no dominant species. However, certain social insects showed considerable promise, and the file might end with the note: "Intelligence may be emerging on this planet. Suggest that intervals between surveys be reduced to a million years."

Very well, you may ask—suppose we encounter beings who judge, condemn and execute us as dispassionately, and with as little effort, as we spray a pool of mosquito larvae with DDT? I must admit that the possibility exists, and the logical answer—that their reasons will no doubt be excellent —is somewhat lacking in appeal. However, this prospect seems remote. I do not believe that any culture can advance, for more than a few centuries at a time, on a technological front alone. Morals and ethics must not lag behind science, otherwise the social system will breed poisons which will cause its certain destruction. I believe therefore that with superhuman knowledge must go equally great compassion and tolerance. In this I may be utterly wrong: the future may yet belong to forces which we should call cruel and evil. Whatever we may hope, we cannot be certain that human aspirations and ideals have universal validity. This we can discover in one way only, and the philosophical mind will be willing to pay the price of knowledge.

I have mentioned before how limited our picture of the Universe must be so long as we are confined to this Earth alone. But the story does not end there. Our impressions of reality are determined, perhaps more than we imagine, by the senses through which we make contact with the external world. How utterly different our cosmologies would have been had Nature economized with us, as she has done with other creatures, and given us eyes incapable of seeing the stars! Yet how pitiably limited are the eyes we do possess, tuned as they are to a single octave in an endless spectrum! The world in which we live is drenched with invisible radiations, from the microwaves which we have just discovered coming from Sun and stars, to the cosmic rays whose origin is still one of the prime mysteries of modern physics. These things we have discovered within the last generation, and we cannot guess what still lies beneath the threshold of the senses—though recent discoveries in paranormal psychology hint that the search may be only beginning.

The races of other worlds will have senses and philosophies very different from our own. To recall Plato's famous analogy, we are prisoners in a cave, gathering our impressions of the outside world from shadows thrown upon the walls. We may never escape to reach that outer reality, but one day we may hope to meet other prisoners in adjoining caves, where the shadows may be very different and where we may learn far more than we could ever do by our own unaided efforts.

These are deep waters, and it is time to turn back to the shore, to leave the distant dream for the present reality of fuels and motors, of combustion-chamber pressures and servomechanisms. Yet I make no apology for discussing these remote vistas at some length, if only to show the triviality of the viewpoint which regards interplanetary travel as a schoolboy adventure of no more real value than the scaling of some hitherto inaccessible mountain. The adventure is there, it is true, and that is good in itself—but it is only a small part of a much greater whole.

Not so shortsighted, but equally false is the view expressed by Professor C. S. Lewis, who has written of would-be astronauts in this unflattering fashion—"The destruction or enslavement of other species in the universe, if such there are, is to these minds a welcome corollary."* In case there are any to whom this prospect still appeals, I would point out that empires, like atomic bombs, are self-liquidating assets. Dominance by force leads to revolution, which in the long run, even if indirectly, must be successful. Humane government leads eventually to self-determination and equality, as the classic case of the British Empire has shown. Commonwealths alone can be stable and enduring, but empires must always contain the seeds of their own dissolution.

The desire to give a comprehensive picture of the outcome of astronautics has compelled me to range—not unwillingly —over an enormous field. However, I do not wish anyone to think that the possibilities we have been discussing need

* *Perelandra* (*Voyage to Venus*). Professor Lewis's more recent views are discussed in "Of Space and the Spirit" (page 174).

come in this century, or the next, or the next. Yet any of them may arise, at any time, as soon as the first ships begin to leave the Earth. Man's first contact with other intelligent races may lie as far away in times as the building of the pyramids—or it may be as near as the discovery of X rays.

Of this, at least, we may be fairly certain. Barring accidents—the most obvious of which I need not specify—the exploration of the planets will be in full swing as this century draws to its close. To examine them in any detail, and to exploit their possibilities fully, will take hundreds of years. But Man being what he is, when his first ship circles down into the frozen wastes of Pluto, his mind will already be bridging the gulf still lying between him and the stars.

Interplanetary distances are a million times as great as those to which we are accustomed in everyday life, but interstellar distances are a millionfold greater still. Before them even light is a hopeless laggard, taking years to pass from one star to its neighbor. How Man will face this stupendous challenge I do not know; but face it one day he will. Professor J. D. Bernal was, I believe, the first to suggest that one solution might lie in the use of artificial planets, little self-contained worlds embarking upon journeys which would last for generations.* Olaf Stapledon has expanded this theme in *Star Maker*, one of the greatest of his fantasies, but the thought of these tiny bubbles of life, creeping from star to star on their age-long journeys, carrying whole populations doomed never to set foot upon any planet, never to know the passage of the seasons or even the interchange of night and day, is one from which we might well recoil in horror. However, those who would make such journeys would have outlooks very different from our own and we cannot judge their minds by our standards.

These speculations, intriguing though they are, will hardly concern mankind in this century. We may, I think confidently expect that it will be a hundred years at least before confinement to the Solar System produces very marked signs of claustrophobia.

Our survey is now finished. We have gone as far as is possible, at this moment of time, in trying to assess the impact of astronautics upon human affairs. I am not unmindful of the

* See "The Planets Are Not Enough" (page 54).

fact that fifty years from now, instead of preparing for the conquest of the outer planets, our grandchildren may be dispossessed savages clinging to the fertile oases in a radioactive wilderness. Yet we must keep the problems of today in their true proportions. They are of vital—indeed of supreme—importance, since they can destroy our civilization and slay the future before its birth. But if we survive them, they will pass into history and the time will come when they will be as little remembered as the causes of the Punic Wars. The crossing of space—even the sense of its imminent achievement in the years before it comes—may do much to turn men's minds outward and away from their present tribal squabbles. In this sense the rocket, far from being one of the destroyers of civilization, may provide the safety valve that is needed to preserve it.

This point may be of the utmost importance. By providing an outlet for man's exuberant and adolescent energies, astronautics may make a truly vital contribution to the problems of the present world. Space flight does not even have to be achieved for this to happen. As soon as there is a general belief in its possibility, that belief will begin to color men's psychological outlook. In many ways, the very dynamic qualities of astronautics are in tune with the restless, expansive spirit of our age.

In this essay I have tried to show that the future development of mankind, on the spiritual no less than the material plane, is bound up with the conquest of space. To what may be called—using the words in the widest possible sense—the liberal scientific mind, I believe these arguments to be unanswerable. The only real criticism that may be raised against them is the quantitative one that the world is not yet ready for such changes. It is hard not to sympathize with this view, which may be correct, but I have given my reasons for thinking otherwise.

The future of which I have spoken is now being shaped by men working with slide rules in quiet offices, and by men taking instrument readings amid the savage roar of harnessed jets. Some are engineers, some are dreamers—but many are both. The time will come when they can say with T. E. Lawrence: "All men dream; but not equally. Those who dream by night in the dusty recesses of their minds wake in the day to find that it was vanity: but the dreamers of the day are dangerous men, for they may act their dream with open eyes, to make it possible."

Thus it has always been in the past, for our civilization is no more than the sum of all the dreams that earlier ages have brought to fulfillment. And so it must always be, for if men cease to dream, if they turn their backs upon the wonder of the Universe, the story of our race will be coming to an end.

In the following three pieces I have attempted to bring home the realities of space travel by considering what the tourists of the twenty-first century will meet when vacationing on the Moon, Mars or a satellite hotel. These articles were commissioned, with considerable foresight, by *Holiday* Magazine almost five years before the launching of the first Sputnik, and I have reproduced them here with only one alteration—the addition of the letters U.S.S.R. . . .

In attempting to give close-ups of the Moon and Mars I have, obviously, had to go beyond the limits of known facts; the best telescopes cannot bring us to within less than 50,000 miles of Mars, or 250 miles of the Moon. My comments on extraterrestrial life forms are therefore purely speculative, but I have been careful not to let them conflict with present-day knowledge.

Much of the material in these three articles has been used to provide the background of *Islands in the Sky*, *Earthlight* and *The Sands of Mars*.

★ VACATION IN VACUUM
★

 ★ When the U.S. and U.S.S.R. started building the first satellite stations, back in the 1960's, the idea that they would one day become health resorts and embarkation points for space-bound vacationers would have seemed slightly fantastic. Yet it was no more fantastic, of course, than the fact that since the beginning of the century the human race had deserted the sea and lifted its commerce into the air. If anyone had dared to prophesy *that* miracle when the Wright Brothers made their first nervous hop in 1903, he would have been laughed to scorn. And even fifty years later, though there were many who realized that space stations might have military and scientific uses, there were very few who looked beyond these to the day when they would become part of everyday life.

Well, perhaps that is a slight exaggeration. Even today, relatively few people have actually *been* to a space station, but there can be nobody who has not seen one with his own eyes. If you live near the equator you have a fine selection to choose from: you can see not only the outer stations but the close refueling satellites that hug the edge of the atmosphere, and are so near the Earth that the curve of the planet hides them from observers in high latitudes. In the daytime they are bright stars, easily visible when the sky is clear, sweeping from horizon to horizon in a matter of minutes. And, of course, they move backward, from west to east, because they race round their tight little orbits so much more quickly than the Earth itself turns on its axis.

At night, they are the brightest stars in the sky, and you can see them move even as you watch. You'll have to look for them low down near the horizon, for as they rise up they disappear into Earth's vast, invisible shadow, winking suddenly out of existence as they go into eclipse and no longer catch the light of the Sun. Sometimes, if you are lucky, you may see a star snuffed out for a few seconds as a space station moves silently across it up there in the emptiness beyond the atmosphere. But the stations are so tiny, and the sky so vast, that you'll have to watch for many nights before you'll see this happen.

Let's go up there into the shining darkness of space, into that paradoxical world where intense heat and unimaginable cold exist together, where dawn and dusk are separated by minutes, not by hours. Yet before we begin the journey, we'll glance back for a moment into the twentieth century, to remind ourselves how so much we now take for granted first came into being.

It was around 1925 that scientists first became seriously interested in space stations as refueling stops for interplanetary rockets. Back at that time, of course, there weren't any rockets—interplanetary or otherwise—and the general public never heard about the idea. It didn't hit the headlines until 1948, soon after the end of the Second World War. The United States military experts had been studying the results of German war research, and had been staggered by what they found. They were now seriously investigating, the Secretary of Defense announced, the possibilities of "space platforms" for military use.

Looking at the newspapers of that time, it's amusing to note the reactions. Many editors asked sarcastically how such platforms could possibly stay up there in the sky. Apparently they'd never bothered to consider how the Moon "stayed up," and so had not realized that the proposed artificial satellites would obey exactly the same laws as the natural ones.

Slowly during the 1950's and '60's, the idea was accepted by the general public as well as the military. As rockets reached greater speeds and altitudes, the goal of the Earth satellite vehicle came nearer to realization, until at last a few instruments were flung out into space, never to return to the atmosphere. That was the first frail rung on the ladder that would lead to the planets.

It was still many years before real man-carrying space stations, and not mere automatic missiles, were constructed from prefabricated parts ferried up by rocket and assembled in space. By the end of the twentieth century there were dozens of military reconnaissance units, meteorological stations and astronomical observatories circling the Earth at various distances, carrying crews of up to twenty men in conditions almost as cramped as in the old-time submarines. They were the first forerunners of the spacious orbital cities we have today—the nuclei around which the later satellites were built, just as on Earth itself great capitals once grew from ancient villages or fortified camps.

The ordinary space traveler sees only the inner station— Space Station One—as he transfers from the Earth ferry rocket to the liner that's taking him to Mars or Venus. It's the nearest of all the satellites, a mere three hundred miles up—too close, therefore, to give one a really good view of Earth. If you want to see the planet as a whole, you've got to travel out to one of the more distant stations. We'll start our tour, therefore, more than ten thousand miles out, in the most luxurious of all the satellites—Sky Hotel.

Even today, with all our modern developments in rocketry, it's highly doubtful if a hotel in space would be a commercial proposition. However, Sky Hotel draws its income from many subsidiary sources. It's not merely patronized from Earth—the staffs from the other satellites take their vacations there, as it's cheaper for them to do that than to pay the fares down to Earth *and* up again. Moreover, Sky Hotel has pretty large shares in the relay stations, which we'll be visiting later in our trip.

The hotel is in two sections—the part with gravity and the part without. When you first see it from your approaching rocket, you'll think you're about to land on the planet Saturn. Hanging there in space ahead of you is a great ball, with a ring surrounding it but not touching it at any point. The ball is motionless, while the ring slowly revolves.

When the pilot has jockeyed the rocket over to the ball, you'll realize just how big the hotel is. Your ship will seem like a toy when it couples itself up to the mooring socket on the axis of the station, and the air locks are joined together so that you can go aboard. The hotel staff will collect both you and your luggage, for most people are pretty helpless under zero gravity for the first few hours. But, believe me, it's an experience worth getting used to.

Sky Hotel has, by ingenious design, managed to get the best of both worlds. Most vacationers go up there to enjoy the fun and games under zero-gee—but weightlessness is not so amusing when you want to eat a meal or take a bath, and some people find it impossible to sleep under free-fall conditions. Hence the dual-purpose design of the hotel. The central ball contains the gymnasiums and that fantastic swimming pool we'll be visiting presently, while over in the ring are the bedrooms, lounges and restaurant. As the ring rotates, centrifugal force gives everyone inside it a feeling of weight which can't be distinguished from the real thing. It's not so powerful, though—at the outer rim of the hotel you'll weigh only half as much as you would on Earth.

And there's one other difference between gravity home on Earth and the imitation variety in the hotel. Because "Up" always points to the center of the ring—to the invisible axle on which it turns—all the floors are curved, like the inside of a drum. If you could see right across the hotel—and maybe it's just as well that you can't—you see that the people on the other side were upside down, with their heads pointing toward you.

It's only in the Sky Grill—the largest room in the ring—that this effect is at all noticeable. When you're dining, your table seems to be at the bottom of a smoothly curving valley, while everyone else is sitting at improbable angles further up the slope. The more distant they are from you, the more canted toward you they will be, until eventually it seems that they must be glued to the wall. It's a fascinating sight watching a waiter come down the slope with a trayful of beers. At first you won't be able to believe your eyes—why don't the glasses spill? Then as he approaches he'll veer over to what you—but nobody else—consider to be the vertical, and you'll breathe a sigh of relief.

Of course, there's nothing mysterious about all this. Centrifugal force can produce exactly the same effect down on Earth if you whirl a bucket at the end of a rope. But I advise you to do the experiment out of doors, and to use water rather than beer.

Most of the hotel's residents divide their time more or less equally between the gee and the zero-gee parts—between the ring and the ball, in other words. The kids are an exception—it's a job luring them away from weightlessness, even for meals, so they spend almost all their time in the ball. There is a snack-bar over there, where you can get drinks served in plastic bulbs so that you can squirt the liquid straight into your mouth. That's the theory—and it works, too. But the kids usually prefer less efficient methods, and promptly empty their bulbs into the air. It's quite a sight watching a budding space cadet chasing a ball of Coke as it drifts slowly from point to point, and eventually splatters messily on one of the walls.

Traveling between the stationary ball and the spinning ring that surrounds it is another of the novelties of space-station life. The trip's made in a kind of pressurized elevator cage, running round a track on the inside of the ring. It's a queer sensation, feeling your weight ebb away as you move across to the ball and centrifugal force vanishes.

The hotel is full of ingenious mechanisms and gadgets like this. Most of them you'll take for granted and may never even see unless you get one of the engineers to take you behind the scenes. Then you may be shown round the air-purifiers that crack the carbon dioxide, so that there's very little loss of oxygen to make good by shipments from Earth.

If they fail, there's a big enough reserve to last until the hotel can be evacuated—or the plant repaired.

Almost as important is the heat-regulating apparatus. Out in space, in direct sunlight, an object can reach a temperature of three or four hundred degrees F. on its "day" side—while the "night" side can be a couple of hundred degrees *below* zero. By circulating air through the double walls of the hotel, these temperature extremes are eliminated.

Ignoring such activities as poker and canasta, which are highly independent of gravity, there are two classes of recreation aboard the hotel. In the ring you can play most of the games that are found on Earth—with suitable modifications. The billiard tables, for example, have to be curved slightly: at first sight it looks as if they dip down the middle, but in this radial gravity field, this makes them behave like flat surfaces. You very quickly get used to this sort of thing, though it may throw off your game for a while when you return to Earth.

However, since there seems little point in going out into space to indulge in terrestrial-type sports, most of the excess energy in Sky Hotel is expended in the zero-gee rooms aboard the ball. The one thing that nobody misses is a chance to do some flying—*real* flying, of the kind we've all dreamed about at some time or another. You may feel a little foolish as you fasten the triangular wings between your ankles and wrists and secure the free ends to your belt. Certainly your first few strokes will start you turning helplessly over and over in the air. But in a few hours you'll be flying like a bird—and much less effortlessly. By the way, the crash helmet that goes with the wings is not just an ornament. It may prevent your knocking yourself out if you get up too much speed and don't notice how near the wall you are.

Some of the zero-gee ballets, with special lighting effects, that the expert performers can execute are unbelievably beautiful, like fairyland filmed in slow motion. Even if you've already seen them on TV, don't miss an opportunity of attending an actual performance at the hotel.

When you've earned your wings in the amusing series of tests that entitles you to your "Spacehound's Certificate," you'll probably want to take part in such sports as zero-gee basketball or three-dimensional miniature golf. Many terrestrial games have been adapted, with interesting variations, to conditions of weightlessness, but there are also dozens of sports and tricks that have no counterpart on Earth.

For example, there's the quite exhausting game you can play where everyone puts on wings and the winner's the one who can collect the largest number of scattered water drops into a single sphere—*and* bring it back to goal before his opponents tear it to pieces.

Talking about water drops leads me, inevitably, to the hotel's most incredible novelty—its famous swimming pool. Any resemblance to similarly described places on Earth is not merely coincidental—it's nonexistent.

When you go to the "pool" you'll find yourself in a big spherical chamber about sixty feet across, almost filled by what is claimed—probably correctly—to be the largest single drop of water in existence. You won't be particularly surprised to see people swimming round and round inside the sphere, but what *will* astonish you is the sight of a group in its center talking and laughing together and perhaps even taking refreshments. Even in space, you'll say to yourself, people still have to breathe!

To settle the mystery, dive into the drop and swim through it. When you've gone about twenty feet, and are still some distance from the center, you'll break through another water surface and find yourself in a hollow space about ten feet across, breathing ordinary air. Yes—you're inside a bubble! It can't escape from the inside of the drop, because only when there is an "Up" can bubbles rise in a liquid. So the swimming pool is really a huge hollow shell of water, and you can sit quietly at the very center and watch your friends sporting like fish all around you.

I *have* seen people smoking in the middle of the pool, though that's against regulations as it's liable to overtax the little air purifier that floats at the exact center of the bubble.

Incidentally keeping the water clean presents some headaches, and you'll notice eight large pipes leading into the giant drop at points equally spaced over its surface. Water flows in and out of these at carefully adjusted rates, so that the shell of liquid always remains the same size.

When you're tired of swimming, you can spend a good many happy hours in the observation lounge, simply watching the Earth and stars. There are no windows in the ring, because it would be rather disconcerting to see the heavens around you revolving at such a rate. So you'll have to do all your stargazing from the nonrotating ball.

From ten thousand miles out, the Earth is just small enough to fill your field of vision completely, and you can see everything except the extreme polar regions. Even to the naked eye, it's a source of endless enchantment. In the nine hours that the hotel takes to complete its orbit, you'll see the Earth change from new to full and back again—going through the phases that the Moon takes a whole month to complete. The sight of the dawn down there, as the Sun comes blasting up through the incandescent mists at the edge of the atmosphere and Earth grows swiftly from a hairline crescent to a huge glowing disk, is something no amount of repetition can ever stale.

When you've had your fill of gazing through the observation windows, you'll turn to the telescopes. Some of them can magnify up to a thousand times, so you'll feel that you're hanging only ten miles above the surface of the Earth. If there's no cloud, it's amazing how much minute detail you can see. Towns and cities are easy; even single large buildings can be detected under favorable conditions. But don't believe anyone who tells you that they've been able to see individual men! That's only possible from the inner satellites, a mere few hundred miles up.

It's interesting to study the effect of these novel surroundings on your companions. Human beings are incredibly adaptable, and for most of the time the guests in Sky Hotel enjoy themselves in the same uninhibited way as if they were down on Earth. But from time to time you'll catch them looking thoughtfully at the stars, realizing that *this* is space— *this* is the Universe. They'll have become suddenly aware that the familiar Earth, with its gravity and its air and its oceans, and its teeming, multitudinous life, is a freak, an incredible rarity; 99.999999 . . . . . . per cent of the cosmos is emptiness and night.

That realization can affect people in two ways. It can depress them when they think how puny Man is against the Universe—or it can exhilarate them when they consider his courage in attempting to conquer it.

Moving in almost exactly the same orbit as the hotel, but fifty miles away from it, is the newest and largest of the space hospitals—Haven IV. It's often possible to arrange a trip across in one of the low-powered rocket shuttles that ply between the orbits of the various stations, and sometimes there are official conducted tours of the hospital. Most of the patients on Haven are heart cases, recuperating under conditions where physical effort is so much less than on Earth and their weakened hearts haven't got to pump pounds of blood up and down the body twenty-four hours a day. The first rocketeeers, crushed in their acceleration couches under the strain of blast-off, would have been very surprised to know how soon cardiac sufferers were to make the same trip. Of course, the patients all travel under deep anesthesia and don't know a thing about it.

Haven IV is a single giant disk, slowly turning on its axis so that the outer rim "gravity" has the same value as on Earth. As you go toward the center and the speed of rotation decreases, the synthetic gravity weakens as well, until at the very center you have complete weightlessness. New patients start their treatment near the axis of the hospital, in wards where gravity is maybe a tenth as powerful as it is on Earth, and move outward toward normal weight as their condition improves. Sometimes they never recover sufficiently to return to Earth—but even these severe cases can settle down on the Moon and get along happily with a sixth of Earth's gravity.

Besides the heart cases, the space hospitals specialize in polio victims, as well as people who have lost their legs and would be virtually helpless down on Earth. There are quite a number of legless men working permanently on the space stations. Often they are more agile than those who are not disabled—they haven't so much useless weight to drag around!

Quite recently, Haven IV has started to deal with severe burns. It doesn't take much imagination to realize how treatment and recuperation can be speeded when the patient can float freely in space and no longer has to lie on his dressings.

No wonder, therefore, that it's been said that the four space hospitals have already repaid humanity all the billions that the conquest of space has cost. And I haven't even mentioned the fundamental medical research they've made possible, particularly through the studies of giant microbes that could only be bred under zero-gee conditions.

From the observation lounge of the Sky Hotel you can see all the inner stations as they pass between you and Earth, moving on their smaller, swifter orbits far more rapidly than you do. Sometimes, when you are looking through a telescope at the lights of some city on the night side of the Earth, you may be surprised to see a tiny brilliant star explode against the darkness and start moving purposefully out into space. You'll have caught one of the interplanetary liners at the moment of take-off, as it pulls away from its refueling station and begins its long journey. And sometimes you may see the glare of one of the big freighter rockets as it starts the climb up from Earth—that two-hundred-mile haul that requires so much more effort than all the millions of miles between the planets.

Down there between you and Earth are the met stations, charting the weather over the entire planet so that we know now, nine times out of ten, exactly what's going to happen during the next forty-eight hours. (The meteorologists are still worried about that odd tenth time, but they swear they're going to get it licked one of these days.) And there are the big space labs, carrying out all sorts of experiments that could never be done on Earth, where no amount of money could buy you a perfect vacuum as many miles across as you cared to specify. Last, but perhaps most important of all, are the astronomical observatories with their vast, floating mirrors, scores of feet across, peering out across the billions of light-years and no longer half blinded by the murk and haze of the atmosphere.

You may feel rather superior to these lower satellites as you look down upon them from your ten-thousand-mile-high eyrie. But if you do, then remember that the outermost of all Earth's man-made moonlets are twelve thousand miles beyond you. I mean of course, the three relay stations which now carry all the long-range TV and radio traffic of the planet.

At this height of twenty-two thousand miles, a satellite takes exactly twenty-four hours to go round its orbit, so the entire huge triangle of the relay chain rotates in synchronism with Earth, just as if it were fixed to it by invisible spokes. That's why, once you've aimed your TV antenna at the nearest relay up there in the sky, you need never move it again. And you can get your pictures without any interference, and from any spot in the world—something that would have seemed incredible when TV was first invented.

Sometimes you can thumb a lift on a shuttle up to one of the relay stations. Out there, more than twenty thousand miles above the Earth, you'll really feel you're on the frontier of space. But don't forget that this is only a tenth of the distance to our nearest neighbor, the Moon—and much less than a thousandth of the distance to Mars or Venus, even at their closest approach. So when you get back to Earth, don't be too boastful about your achievements—at least until you've made quite sure that there are no *real* spacehounds in the party.

More seriously, there's one point you must watch when you're home again. Take things *very* easily for the first few days. Remember, we've got a little thing called gravity down here, and the tricks you can play in Sky Hotel won't work so well back on Earth. You can't cross Fifth Avenue, for instance, by stepping out at the two-hundredth floor of Planet Tower and launching yourself in an easterly direction. (Take my word for it—it's been tried.) Even in your own home, you may find yourself treating the stairs with quite unjustified contempt, so this warning is by no means as superfluous as it seems.

Finally, I've been asked to deny a canard which has been causing the hotel management much grief. Luigi, *chef de cuisine,* is particularly upset by the slander which he's convinced has been put out by rival establishments on Earth. It's completely untrue that the guests at the hotel have to live on compressed foods and vitamin pills, like the first space pioneers. The meals are as good as anything you can get on Earth. They may not actually weigh as much, but I can assure you, from personal experience, that they're every bit as satisfying. . . .

★ JOURNEY BY EARTHLIGHT
★

★ Just a hundred years ago, back in 1976,* the first men landed on the Moon, and the age of space flight began. During the last few years, it must be admitted, the glamor of more romantic places like Mars and Venus has diverted attention from our satellite. Perhaps it's so close that we tend to take it for granted, just as no New Yorker ever bothers to go to the top of Planet Tower to see what his city looks like from half a mile up. Moreover, until very recently few people went to the Moon unless they were scientists or technicians on official business.

Two things have changed this. Now that the necessary facilities exist, the Lunar Commission is encouraging a limited tourist trade, though for the moment it will be restricted to the Earthward face of the Moon. The second factor, of course, is the establishment of Pasteur City, which is likely to have a profound effect on medical research and even, ultimately, on human society.

Looking back on it from our vantage point, it is obvious that the first landing on the Moon was an anticlimax. Everyone had been expecting it for almost half a century: it had been the theme of countless books and movies, and rockets had been getting closer and closer for twenty years before the final touchdown was made. Moreover, no one had expected to find very much on the Moon—and for a while they weren't disappointed. The general impression, through most of the twentieth century, was that the Moon was completely dead and unchanging—a cosmic slag heap of interest only to geologists and astronomers. It might be useful as an observatory and a fueling stop on the road to

* This seemed wildly optimistic in the early 1950's. Today, 1970 would be a safer guess.

the planets, but otherwise it was not a very valuable piece of real estate.

To see how accurate that first impression was, imagine you're aboard the passenger ship *Archimedes* as it drops down toward the rugged lunar landscape. The journey from Space Station One, just outside the Earth's atmosphere, has taken less than ten hours. Once, it lasted almost five days, but now that atomic propulsion has been perfected, fuel economy is no longer at a premium and the crossing can be made at much higher speeds.

However many times you do it, a landing on the Moon is an awe-inspiring experience, totally different from the long glide through the upper atmosphere which brings you down on planets like Earth or Mars. The lunar landing must be made by rockets alone, at the end of an interminable fall which is checked only when you are within a hundred miles of that jagged, pock-marked landscape. Then the silence will be broken as the rockets thunder into life, and your returning weight will force you down into your seat. Through the observation window—if you're lucky enough to be near one—you'll see the white-hot pillar of flame which is checking your headlong fall. The squat and stubby *Archimedes* will look like a giant spider as it descends, outthrust landing legs spread to take up the shock of impact.

Touchdown itself will be indicated only by the final cessation of thrust, and a ringing silence as the rockets die. Then there will be a curious, heaving motion as the long hydraulic cylinders in the undercarriage absorb the ship's momentum. It will last for less than a second, but if the landing has been badly off the vertical you'll think for a minute that you're aboard a boat in a choppy sea. Luckily it doesn't last long enough for anyone to be seasick. . . .

The very first question that everybody asks when they find themselves on the Moon is "where are all the mountains?" For hours they'll have seen those great peaks coming closer and closer: they'll have watched the crater walls rise around them until the summits seem to tower above the falling ship. And then, when the flurry of dust and flame has died away, the *Archimedes* will be standing on a rocky plain, with only a few low hills in sight. Though you are in the center of a mountain-fringed plain, the steep curve of the Moon's surface has hidden the surrounding walls from view. It will take you some time to get used to this nearness of the horizon, caused by the fact that the Moon is only a quarter the size of the Earth.

The *Archimedes* will land in the Sinus Medii—a small plain at the exact center of the Moon's visible face. This region is of enormous geological interest, for it is surrounded by crevasses of up to a hundred miles in length. Through these gigantic fissures, men have been able to penetrate far into the crust and hence the area is one of great mining activity. Though no sound can exist where there is no atmosphere to carry it, you'll sometimes feel the ground shake as blasting charges are let off round the colossal canyon known as the Hyginus Cleft.

Sinus Medii means "Central Bay"; though of course there is no free water on the Moon, such terms as bay, sea, ocean and lake were used only by the early astronomers and have stuck so thoroughly that no one can change them now. To make matters more confusing to newcomers, the Latin and English versions are used indiscriminately. It may take you some time to realize, for example, that Palus Somnii is the same place as the Marsh of Sleep. Though there have been several attempts to tidy up lunar nomenclature, nothing has come of them and we're stuck with the five-hundred-year-old names. Luckily the Moon's other side—which of course was never seen until the first rockets started to land there—isn't littered with remnants of medieval astrology. The great formations there have been named after famous men of modern times, so don't be surprised to encounter Einstein, Churchill, Rutherford, Sibelius, Roosevelt—all of whom have craters more than a hundred miles across.*

The Sinus Medii is not only the main spaceport on this side of the Moon, but also the center for surface transport. All long-distance travel is by monorail, for the Moon is an absolutely ideal place for this type of locomotion. There's no air resistance, so speeds of five hundred miles an hour can be reached with little difficulty. And the low gravity greatly eases the construction problem—the single rail need

* See "The Men on the Moon" (page 159) for a fuller account of lunar nomenclature.

only be supported at wide intervals, and bridges can have enormous spans.

So come aboard the north-bound track to Pasteur City, in the great walled plain of Plato, and take a ride over the most spectacular scenery on the Moon. We'll leave in darkness, a few hours after the beginning of the long lunar night.

The monorail car holds about fifty passengers, and is automatically controlled. Because its weight is too low to give good traction, the driving wheels grip the rail *horizontally* under the pressure of powerful springs. The terminus itself might be a station on Earth: there'll be the usual lines of track, the speakers calling departures and arrivals. But when everyone has come aboard, the car will be sealed and will slide through double doors into a huge air lock. You'll hear the throb of giant pumps as the chamber is evacuated; then the outer door will open and there will be a surge of acceleration as the moonrail's electric motors speed you out of the terminus, onto the surface of the Moon.

If you're lucky, you may see a take-off as you skirt the edge of the spaceport. A night launch from the Moon is an unforgettable sight; its utter soundlessness somehow adds to the effect. The ship will ascend in a cloud of dust blasted up from the plain—a cloud within which the jets will burn like incredibly brilliant suns. As the dust falls behind, the blue-white glare will flood the landscape with a light more fierce even than that of noon. It will ebb away as the ship dwindles against the stars, and will suddenly wink out of existence as the departing vessel reaches escape velocity and cuts its drive.

For the first few hundred miles, the monorail runs over relatively flat country as it heads northeast. Though the Sun has set, the landscape will be brilliantly illuminated by the Earth, just passing its first quarter but already giving a dozen times as much light as the full Moon does to the terrestrial scene. It's a cold light: an arctic radiance that gives not an atom of heat. For it's tinged with the blues and greens of Earth's oceans and clouds; it sparkles from the polar caps that even across a quarter of a million miles of space are too dazzling for the unprotected eye. It's hard to believe that this freezing luminosity really comes from a world of warmth and life.

There's an observation room at the front of the car, curtained off from the light of the main cabin. Unless you're a seasoned, blasé traveler, you'll spend most of your time here, watching the lunar landscape racing past. Ahead of you the single rail, supported by pillars disquietingly far apart, is now running almost due east. Here's another paradox to bother you: the way directions on the Moon have been chosen, the Sun sets in the east, not the west. . . .

The monorail is losing speed as it climbs up out of the shadowed lowlands. At any moment now, you'll overtake the Sun. The line of darkness moves so slowly here that a running man could almost keep abreast of it, and could hold the Sun balanced on the horizon as long as he could maintain his speed.

On your left—that's the south—the broken land falls away in a series of layers as if, a million years ago, the lava welling up from the Moon's molten heart had solidified in successive, weakening waves. It's a scene that chills the soul, yet there are spots on Earth as bleak as this. The Badlands of Arizona are equally desolate; the upper slopes of Everest are still more hostile, for though the temperature here is two hundred degrees below zero, at least there is not eternal ravening wind.

And then—the cliff on your right comes to a sudden halt as if a monstrous chisel had sliced it off the surface of the Moon. You can see clear round to the north: there, marching across the sky in flaming glory, are the peaks of the Apennines, incandescent in the last rays of the hidden Sun. The abrupt blaze of light almost blinds you, and you have to shield your eyes from the glare until you can safely face it. When you look again, the transformation is complete. The stars, which until a moment ago had filled the sky, have vanished. Your contracted pupils can no longer see them: even the glowing Earth now seems no more than a feeble patch of phosphorescence. The glare from the sunlit mountains, still fifty miles away, has eclipsed all other sources of light.

The peaks float in the sky, fantastic pyramids of flame. They seem to have no more connection with the ground beneath them than do the clouds that hover round a sunset on Earth. The line of shadow is so sharp, the lower slopes of the mountains so lost in utter darkness, that only the burning summits have any real existence. It will be hours yet before the last of those proud peaks slips back into the shadow of the Moon and surrenders to the night.

The Apennines are the finest range on this side of the Moon: those summits tower more than twenty thousand feet above the plain, and seem an impassable barrier. But twenty thousand feet on the Moon is equivalent to less than four thousand feet on Earth, and it is possible to ascend vertiginous inclines with impunity. The monorail weaves and climbs through spectacular passes, then drops down the northern slopes into the vast plain of the Mare Imbrium —the Sea of Rains. As you descend into the lowlands, the Sun which your speed has magically conjured up from night sinks again below the edge of the Moon. There is little more to see until you reach Pasteur; you might as well go back into the cabin and join your fellow passengers.

You'll catch your first glimpse of the city as you descend the inner ramparts of Plato—the superb walled plain on the northern border of the Mare. It's strange to think that Man built his first extraterrestrial cities on distant Mars, not on his nearest neighbor in space. But the incentive was greater, the technical problems less. Now that they have been overcome, we can expect to see many more cities on the Moon.

The first lunar bases were entirely underground; many of them still are. By digging a few feet into the interior one can completely avoid the four-hundred-degree temperature change between day and night. The first colonists were also frightened of meteors, and decided to take no chances against bombardment from space.

We know now that meteors are no more common on the Moon than they are on Earth. For the Moon has an atmosphere: true, it's a billion times less dense than ours, but because of the lower gravity it extends much further into space. As far as breathing it is concerned, you might just as well be in a vacuum—but this tenuous envelope has two very important practical uses. It's a first-class meteor screen—and it provides an ionosphere like Earth's, reflecting radio waves round the curve of the planet so that long-distance communication is possible.

Pasteur City consists of a dozen pressure domes, linked together by air locks, a few miles from the north wall of Plato. One of the domes is transparent, so that the residents can watch the pageant of the changing heavens, can see the long dawn break above the mountains—and can watch the seasons come and go on the world to which they can never return.

Yet it is quite wrong to think of Pasteur City as a home for convalescents, like the space-station hospitals circling Earth. Almost all its twenty thousand inhabitants live normal, unrestricted lives. But they could do so only here, where they weigh no more than thirty pounds and the strain on hearts and muscles is correspondingly reduced.

Like all great advances in medical science, the founding of Pasteur City has opened up new and unsuspected frontiers. If people suffering from chronic heart disease can live out their normal span under the Moon's low gravity, what will be the expectation of an ordinary, healthy man? No one talks too much about this, but there's an air of suppressed excitement among the doctors studying the matter. Some of them have been heard to say that old age can now be postponed until far into the second century. If this is true, and the technical problems of supporting a large lunar population can be overcome—well, we can expect some interesting social changes.

Pasteur looks like an ideal center for the tourist trade when it starts to develop, for the Mare Imbrium is one of the most beautiful regions of the Moon. The city itself is still somewhat deficient in luxuries, since the effort to become self-supporting has absorbed most of its energy. Oxygen and water have to be extracted by chemical means from the lunar rocks—in which, luckily, they are fairly common. Food is produced under acres of glass in the huge hydroponic farms, where nutrient solutions flow through pressurized tubes during the fourteen days of continuous sunlight. You'll be surprised to find how tasteful some of these synthetic foods are, but you'll make yourself unpopular if you ask for steaks or chops.

In Pasteur City you'll encounter a practical problem that won't have bothered you greatly elsewhere. At the spaceport back in the Sinus Medii, and on the monorail trip, you will have been in fairly cramped surroundings, and won't have been able to perform those athletic feats which the earlier writers about the Moon loved to emphasize. It's not very practical, for instance, to jump twenty feet high when the ceiling is only a yard above your head. But in Pasteur City, under the domes, you will have your first real opportunity to show off.

Well, take it easy. Don't go up until you are sure you know how to come down. It's all too simple to turn over in flight and land on your head—which will damage you just as much as it would on Earth. Should you wear one of those lead belts which are recommended to visitors during their first few days on the Moon? That's up to you; try one, by all means—it may save you from injury through carelessness. But there's a snag, which many people don't realize, about loading yourself down with lead. Whereas *weight* on the Moon is reduced to a sixth, *inertia* is exactly the same. Your hundred pounds of lead will help keep you on the ground and will be no burden when you are standing still. But as soon as you start or stop, or try to change direction, it will feel exactly what it is—a hundred pounds of lead!

Personally, I think the best thing to do is to accept your weight for what it is, and learn to reduce muscular effort accordingly. Your first attempts to take strides of normal length will look somewhat prissy and mincing, but you'll soon get used to it.

Since you won't have come all the way to the Moon to look at other human beings, you'll want to spend as much time as you can outside the city. Short-range lunar transport is carried out by tractors—pressurized vehicles with large balloon tires and caterpillar treads that can negotiate any ground that isn't actually vertical. (Even that's an unfair restriction; tractors have often hauled themselves up cliffs with their power winches.) They are virtually spaceships on wheels, and prospectors live in the larger ones for weeks at a time.

Because rockets are hardly practical for this kind of work, the detailed examination of the Moon has depended almost entirely on these tough little vehicles. Some have now been turned into observation cars, and are already operating around Plato, carrying sight-seers from Pasteur City. The most popular trips are those along the foothills of the Alps, and over the Pole to the hidden face of the Moon.

The Alpine excursion runs south from Plato to the great mountain of Pico, rearing itself to a height of eight thousand feet above the plain. It now stands in splendid isolation, but was once part of a mighty crater wall destroyed by volcanic action when the Moon was young.

Then the tractor will swing west for two hundred miles until it comes to Mount Blanc, the great sentinel standing guard at the entrance to the extraordinary Alpine Valley. This weird formation, eighty miles long, slices through the Alps like a railroad cutting, and even now we do not know exactly how it was caused. Entering it is like driving into the Grand Canyon—except that *this* valley is almost perfectly straight and was certainly not produced by the action of water.

If you are a really expert mountaineer, and are prepared to sign the necessary waivers, you may be allowed to try your skill on some of the Alpine peaks. At first sight, your reduced weight will seem a great advantage—and so it is, since you can easily lift yourself with one arm. But low gravity can also induce carelessness; a sixty-foot fall on the Moon is as dangerous as a ten-foot one on Earth—more dangerous, in fact, since there is always the risk of damaging your spacesuit. Although these suits have now reached a high degree of perfection—they are practically foolproof, and can keep a man alive for twenty-four hours—no one claims that they are exactly comfortable, and they prevent free and unimpeded movement. With all your equipment, your Earth weight when you start climbing will be about fifty pounds.

One surprising fact about lunar slopes and mountains is that, on the whole, they are not as steep as on Earth. Because of the absence of weathering, however, they are angular and jagged—there have been no winds or rains to soften their contours. The complete absence of snow or ice removes one major obstacle to climbing, and, when all factors are taken into account, lunar mountaineering, despite its risks, is not more suicidal a pursuit than its terrestrial equivalent.

From the region round Pasteur City, the Earth hangs low in the southern sky, its continents clearly visible and its blanket of atmosphere forming a luminous haze around its edge. It is so near the mountains that you expect it to set at any moment, and it will be a long time before you get used to the idea that it will always be there, fixed in the lunar sky. The Sun and stars rise and set, taking two weeks of Earth time to cross from horizon to horizon; but Earth remains forever motionless, apart from a slight swaying back and forth caused by the fact that the Moon's orbital motion is not perfectly regular. The only change that Earth shows is that of phase, as it waxes to full and wanes to a threadlike crescent. After a while, you will be able to tell the time by that great clock hanging there against the stars. . . .

The stars—yes, they will give you another surprise. Even today, people will tell you that on the Moon you can see Sun and stars in the sky at once. It's a statement which is both true and false. If you look directly at the Sun, you won't see anything else for a long time, and you'll be lucky not to damage your eyes. During daytime on the Moon, if you are out in the open, the glare from the rocks demands the use of sun filters and your pupils will be fully contracted. Consequently, though the stars *are* shining up there in the sky, you won't be able to see them and it will be perfectly black overhead. If you want to look at the stars, step into the shadow of a convenient rock and shield your eyes from all glare around you.

Then, as your vision adapts itself and your pupils enlarge, you'll see the stars come out. First there will be the bright, familiar constellations, then the legions of their faint companions, until at last the whole sky seems packed with glowing dust. All those countless points of light will be shining with a steady, unvarying radiance: none will twinkle or scintillate as they do in the clearest nights on Earth. Now you will understand why all the great observatories are on the Moon: you will realize that, until he had climbed above the atmosphere of his own planet, no man had ever really seen the stars. . . .

Though it was known long before the first landings that the conquest of the Moon would revolutionize astronomy, few people believed that biologists would find anything of interest on our satellite. Yet, as far back as the beginning of the twentieth century, evidence had been accumulating that plant life existed around certain craters, such as Aristarchus and Eratosthenes. There had been curious changes of shading and variable patches of darkness that were hard to explain in any other way.

The explanation was correct. Where the mistake was made was in assuming that any lunar plants would be primitive, when a little thought would have shown that the reverse must be the case. Conditions on the Moon are so severe that only very advanced and sophisticated types of plants exist there—the primitive, unspecialized forms died out aeons ago. Most of the existing vegetation is found in the neighborhood of the great lunar clefts, such as the Herodotus Valley, for traces of carbon dioxide, water vapor and sulphur dioxide occasionally gush out of these fissures— sometimes producing short-lived mists which are visible from Earth. These precious gases are eagerly trapped by the slender, cactuslike plants. They are absorbed through systems of pores and tubes which are virtually air compressors; you can cause great excitement among the plants by deliberately spilling some air from your suit, when the multitudes of pores will start frantically opening and closing.

The lunar plants have another ingenious trick which allows them to trap sunlight without losing water vapor. Their upper parts are studded with tiny "windows" of horny material, transparent to light but impenetrable to gases. Oddly enough, exactly the same technique has been worked out independently by certain plants in the dry African deserts, where in some respects conditions are not so very different from those on the Moon.

Incidentally, no one has yet found any practical use for these plants. Their chemistry contains too much sulphur for them to be edible, but when we have learned more about them they may teach us how to grow our own crops on the unprotected lunar surface—obviously a matter of great practical importance.

The question is often asked: "Is there any evidence for *animal*, as opposed to plant, life on the Moon?" It's true that much of the Moon's twelve million square miles of highly contorted terrain is still unexplored, and there may yet be some surprises in store for us. But it's most unlikely that animal life will be among them. Though biologists have had a lot of fun imagining creatures that could live under lunar conditions, none of them has so far obliged by making an appearance.

One must not be greedy. The Moon has already turned out to be a much more valuable and interesting place than the first pioneers expected. The millions that have been sunk into it are beginning to pay off in terms of knowledge—from the observatories and vacuum labs; of raw materials—from the mines and refueling stations; and of human happiness—from Pasteur City. There were some who feared that when we reached the Queen of Night, her romance and mystery would be destroyed. They need not have worried. We may roof the lunar craters, spread our cities across the dusty seas, build our farms on the Sunward-facing slopes of the mountains. We will not change the essential nature of the Moon. She watched life emerge from the steaming oceans of the dawn; she saw Man embark on the conquest of his own world—and, a little later, the conquest of space itself.

She will still be watching, drawing the tides beneath her, when our descendants have spread so far from home that few could say in what region of the sky lies the ancestral planet Earth. . . .

★ **SO YOU'RE GOING TO MARS?**
★

    ★ So you're going to Mars? That's still quite an adventure—though I suppose that in another ten years no one will think twice about it. Sometimes it's hard to remember that the first ships reached Mars scarcely more than half a century ago, and that our colony on the planet is less than thirty years old. (By the way, don't use *that* word when you get there. Base, settlement, or whatever you like—but not colony, unless you want to hear the ice tinkling all around you.)

I suppose you've read all the forms and tourist literature they gave you at the Department of Extraterrestrial Affairs. But there's a lot you won't learn just by reading, so here are some pointers and background information that may make your trip more enjoyable. I won't say it's right up to date—things change so rapidly and it's a year since I got back from Mars myself—but on the whole you'll find it pretty reliable.

Presumably you're going just for curiosity and excitement—because you want to see what life is like out on the new frontier. It's only fair, therefore, to point out that most of your fellow passengers will be engineers, scientists or administrators traveling to Mars—some of them not for the first time—because they've got a job of work to do. So whatever your achievements here on Earth, it's advisable not to talk too much about them, as you'll be among people who've had to tackle much tougher propositions. I won't say that you'll find them boastful: it's simply that they've got a lot to be proud of, and they don't mind who knows it.

If you haven't booked your passage yet, remember that the cost of the ticket varies considerably according to the relative position of Mars and Earth. That's a complication we don't have to worry about when we're traveling from country to country on our own globe, but Mars can be six times further away at one time than at another. Oddly enough, the shortest trips are the most expensive, since they involve the greatest changes of speed as you hop from one orbit to the other. And in space, speed, not distance, is what costs money.

Incidentally, I'd like to know how you've managed it. I believe the cheapest round trip comes to about $30,000, and unless the firm is backing you or you've got a very elastic expense account—oh, all right, if you don't want to talk about it. . . .

I take it you're O.K. on the medical side. That examination isn't for fun, nor is it intended to scare anyone off. The physical strain involved in space flight is negligible—but you'll be spending at least two months on the trip, and it would be a pity if your teeth or your appendix started to misbehave. See what I mean?

You're probably wondering how you can possibly manage on the weight allowance you've got. Well, it can be done. The first thing to remember is that you don't need to take any suits. There's no weather inside a spaceship—the temperature never varies more than a couple of degrees over the whole trip, and it's held at a fairly high value so that all you'll want is an ultra-lightweight tropical kit. When you get to Mars you'll buy what you need there, and dump it when you return. The great thing to remember is—*only carry the stuff you actually need on the trip.* I strongly advise you to buy one of the complete travel kits—most of the big stores like Abercrombie & Fitch can supply the approved outfits. They're expensive, but will save you money on excess baggage charges.

Take a camera by all means—there's a chance of some unforgettable shots as you leave Earth and when you approach Mars. But there's nothing to photograph on the voyage itself, and I'd advise you to take all your pictures on the outward trip. You can sell a good camera on Mars for five times its price here—and save yourself the cost of freighting it home. They don't mention *that* in the official handouts.

Now that we've brought up the subject of money, I'd better remind you that the Martian economy is quite different from anything you'll meet on Earth. Down here, it doesn't cost you anything to breathe, even though you've got to pay to eat. But on Mars the very air has to be synthesized—they break down the oxides in the ground to do this—so every time you fill your lungs someone has to foot the bill. Food production is planned in the same way— each of the cities, remember, is a carefully balanced eco- logical system, like a well-organized aquarium. No parasites can be allowed, so everyone has to pay a basic tax which entitles him to air, food and the shelter of the domes. The tax varies from city to city, but averages about ten dollars a day. Since everyone earns at least ten times as much as this, they can all afford to go on breathing.

You'll have to pay this tax, of course—and you'll find it rather hard to spend much more money than this. Once the basic needs for life are taken care of, there aren't many luxuries on Mars. When they've got used to the idea of having tourists around, no doubt they'll get organized, but as things are now you'll find that most reasonable requests won't cost you anything. However, I should make arrangements to transfer a substantial credit balance to the Bank of Mars—if you've still got anything left. You can do that by radio, of course, before you leave Earth.

So much for the preliminaries; now some points about the trip itself. The ferry rocket will probably leave from the

New Guinea field, which is about two miles above sea level on the top of the Orange Range. People sometimes wonder why they chose such an out-of-the-way spot. That's simple: it's on the equator, so a ship gets the full thousand-mile-an-hour boost of the Earth's spin as it takes off— and there's the whole width of the Pacific for jettisoned fuel tanks to fall into. And if you've ever *heard* a spaceship taking off, you'll understand why the launching sites have to be a few hundred miles from civilization. . . .

Don't be alarmed by anything you've been told about the strain of blast-off. There's really nothing to it, if you're in good health—and you won't be allowed inside a spaceship unless you are. You just lie down on the acceleration couch, put in your earplugs and relax. It takes over a minute for the full thrust to build up, and by that time you're quite accustomed to it. You'll have some difficulty in breathing, perhaps—it's never bothered me—but if you don't attempt to move you'll hardly feel the increase of weight. What you *will* notice is the noise, which is slightly unbelievable. Still, it only lasts five minutes, and by the end of that time you'll be up in the orbit and the motors will cut out. Don't worry about your hearing; it will get back to normal in a couple of hours.

You won't see a great deal until you get aboard the space station, because there are no viewing ports on the ferry rockets and passengers aren't encouraged to wander around. It usually takes about thirty minutes to make the necessary steering corrections and to match speed with the station; you'll know when that's happened from the rather alarming "clang" as the air locks make contact. Then you can undo your safety belt, and of course you'll want to see what it's like being weightless.

Now, take your time—and do exactly what you're told. Hang on to the guide rope through the air lock and don't try to go flying around like a bird. There'll be plenty of time for that later: there's not enough room in the ferry and if you attempt any of the usual tricks you'll not only injure yourself but may damage the equipment as well.

Space Station One—which is where the ferries and the liners meet to transfer their cargoes—takes just two hours to make one circuit of the Earth. You'll spend all your time in the observation lounge: everyone does, no matter how many times they've been out into space. *I* won't attempt to describe that incredible view; I'll merely remind you that in the hundred and twenty minutes it takes the station to complete its orbit you'll see the Earth wax from a thin crescent to a gigantic multicolored disk—and then shrink again to a black shield eclipsing the stars. As you pass over the night side you'll see the lights of cities down there in the darkness, like patches of phosphorescence. And the stars! You'll realize that you've never really seen them before in your life.

But enough of these purple passages; let's stick to business. You'll probably remain on Space Station One for about twelve hours, which will give you plenty of opportunity to see how you like weightlessness. It doesn't take long to learn how to move around; the main secret it to avoid all violent motions—otherwise you may crack your head on the ceiling. Except, of course, that there isn't a ceiling, since there's no up or down any more. At first you'll find that confusing: you'll have to stop and decide which direction you want to move in, and then adjust your personal reference system to fit. After a few days in space it will be second nature to you.

Don't forget that the station is your last link with Earth. If you want to make any final purchases, or leave something to be sent home—do it then. You won't have another chance for a good many million miles. But beware of buying items that the station shop assures you are "just the thing on Mars."

You'll go aboard the liner when you've had your final medical check, and the steward will show you to the little cabin that will be your home for the next few months. Don't be upset because you can touch all the walls without moving from one spot. You'll only have to sleep there, after all, and you've got the rest of the ship to stretch your legs in.

If you're on one of the larger liners, there'll be about a hundred other passengers and a crew of perhaps twenty. You'll get to know them all by the end of the voyage. There's nothing on Earth quite like the atmosphere in a spaceship. You're a little, self-contained community floating in vacuum millions of miles from anywhere, kept alive in a bubble of plastic and metal. If you're a good mixer, you'll find the experience very stimulating. But it has its disadvantages. The one great danger of space flight is that some prize bore may get on the passenger list—and short of pushing him out of the air lock there's nothing anyone can do about it.

It won't take you long to find your way around the ship and to get used to its gadgets. Handling liquids is the main skill you'll have to acquire: your first attempts at drinking are apt to be messy. Oddly enough, taking a shower is quite simple. You do it in sort of plastic cocoon, and a circulating air current carries the water out at the bottom.

At first the absence of gravity may make sleeping difficult —you'll miss your accustomed weight. That's why the sheets over the bunks have spring tensioning. They'll prevent you drifting out while you sleep, and their pressure will give you a spurious sensation of weight.

But learning to live under zero gravity is something one can't be taught in advance: you have to find out by experience and practical demonstration. I believe you'll enjoy it, and when the novelty's worn off you'll take it completely for granted. Then the problem will be getting used to gravity again when you reach Mars!

Unlike the take-off of the ferry rocket from Earth, the breakaway of the liner from its satellite orbit is so gentle and protracted that it lacks all drama. When the loading and instrument checks have been completed, the ship will uncouple from the space station and drift a few miles away. You'll hardly notice it when the atomic drive goes on—there will be the faintest of vibrations and a feeble sensation of weight. The ship's acceleration is so small, in fact, that you'll weigh only a few ounces, which will scarcely interfere with your freedom of movement at all. Its only effect will be to make things drift slowly to one end of the cabin if they're left lying around.

Although the liner's acceleration is so small that it will take hours to break away from Earth and head out into space, after a week of continuous drive the ship will have built up a colossal speed. Then the motors will be cut out and you'll carry on under your own momentum until you reach the orbit of Mars and have to start thinking about slowing down.

Whether your weeks in space are boring or not depends very much on you and your fellow passengers. Quite a number of entertainments get organized on the voyage, and a good deal of money is liable to change hands before the end of the trip. (It's a curious fact, but the crew usually seems to come out on top.) You'll have plenty of time for reading, and the ship will have a good library of microbooks. There will be radio and TV contact with Earth and Mars for the whole voyage, so you'll be able to keep in touch with things —if you want to.

On my first trip, I spent a lot of my time learning my way around the stars and looking at clusters and nebulae through a small telescope I borrowed from the navigation officer. Even if you've never felt the slightest interest in astronomy before, you'll probably be a keen observer before the end of the voyage. Having the stars all around you— and not merely overhead—is an experience you'll never forget.

As far as outside events are concerned, you realize of course that absolutely nothing can happen during the voyage. Once the drive has cut out, you'll seem to be hanging motionless in space: you'll be no more conscious of your speed than you are of the Earth's seventy thousand miles an hour round the Sun right now. The only evidence of your velocity will be the slow movement of the nearer planets against the background of the stars—and you'll have to watch carefully for a good many hours before you can detect even this.

By the way, I hope you aren't one of those foolish people who are still frightened about meteors. They see that enormous chunk of nickel-steel in New York's American Museum of Natural History and imagine that's the sort of thing you'll run smack into as soon as you leave the atmosphere— forgetting that there's a lot of room in space and that even the biggest ship is a mighty small target. You'd have to sit out there and wait a good many centuries before a meteor big enough to puncture the hull came along—it hasn't happened to a spaceship yet.

One of the big moments of the trip will come when you realize that Mars has begun to show a visible disk. The first feature you'll be able to see with the naked eye will be one of the polar caps, glittering like a tiny star on the edge of the planet. A few days later the dark areas—the so-called seas—will begin to appear, and presently you'll glimpse the prominent triangle of the Syrtis Major. In the week before landing, as the planet swims nearer and nearer, you'll get to know its geography pretty thoroughly.

The braking period doesn't last very long, as the ship has lost a good deal of its speed in the climb outward from the Sun. When it's over you'll be dropping down onto Phobos, the inner moon of Mars—which acts as a natural space station about four thousand miles above the surface of the planet. Though Phobos is only a jagged lump of rock not much bigger than some terrestrial mountains, its reassuring to be in contact with something solid again after so many weeks in space.

When the ship has settled down into the landing cradle, the air lock will be coupled up and you'll go through a connecting tube into the port. Since Phobos is much too small to have an appreciable gravity, you'll still be effectively weightless. While the ship's being unloaded the immigration officials will check your papers. I don't know the point of this; I've never heard of anyone being sent all the way back to Earth after having got this far!

There are two things you mustn't miss at Port Phobos. The restaurant there is quite good; it's very small, and only goes into action when a liner docks, but it does its best to give you a fine welcome to Mars. And after a couple of months you'll have got rather tired of the shipboard menu.

The other item is the centrifuge; I believe that's compulsory now. You go inside and it will spin you up to half a gravity, or rather more than the weight Mars will give you when you land. It's simply a little cabin on a rotating arm, and there's room to walk around inside so that you can practice using your legs again. You probably won't like the feeling; life in a spaceship can make you lazy.

The ferry rockets that will take you down to Mars will be waiting when the ship docks. If you're unlucky you'll hang around at the port for some hours, because they can't carry more than twenty passengers and there are only two ferries in service. The actual descent to the planet takes about three hours—and it's the only time on the whole trip when you'll get any impression of speed. Those ferries enter the atmosphere at over five thousand miles an hour, and go halfway round Mars before they lose enough speed through air resistance to land like ordinary aircraft.

You'll land, of course, at Port Lowell: besides being the largest settlement on Mars it's still the only place that has the facilities for handling spaceships. From the air the plastic pressure domes look like a cluster of bubbles—a very pretty sight when the Sun catches them. Don't be alarmed if one of them is deflated. That doesn't mean that there's been an accident. The domes are let down at fairly frequent intervals so that the envelopes can be checked for leaks. If you're lucky you may see one being pumped up—it's quite impressive.

After two months in a space ship, even Port Lowell will seem a mighty metropolis. (Actually, I believe its population is now well over twenty thousand.) You'll find the people energetic, inquisitive, forthright—and very friendly, unless they think you're trying to be superior.

It's a good working rule never to criticize anything you see on Mars. As I said before, they're very proud of their achievements—and after all you *are* a guest, even if a paying one.

Port Lowell has practically everything you'll find in a city on Earth, though of course on a smaller scale. You'll come across many reminders of "home." For example, the main street in the city is Fifth Avenue—but surprisingly enough you'll find Piccadilly Circus where it crosses Broadway.

The port, like all the major settlements, lies in the dark belt of vegetation that roughly follows the Equator and occupies about half the southern hemisphere. The northern hemisphere is almost all desert—the red oxides that give the planet its ruddy color. Some of these desert regions are very beautiful; they're far older than anything on the surface of our Earth, because there's been little weathering on Mars to wear down the rocks—at least since the seas dried up, more than five hundred million years ago.

You shouldn't attempt to leave the city until you've become quite accustomed to living in an oxygen-rich, low-pressure atmosphere. You'll have grown fairly well acclimatized on the trip, because the air in the spaceship will have been slowly adjusted to conditions on Mars. Outside the domes, the pressure of the natural Martian atmosphere is about equal to that on the top of Mount Everest—and it contains practically no oxygen. So when you go out you'll have to wear a helmet, or travel in one of those pressurized jeeps they call "sand fleas."

Wearing a helmet, by the way, is nothing like the nuisance you'd expect it to be. The equipment is very light and compact, and as long as you don't do anything silly is quite foolproof. As it's most unlikely that you'll ever go out without an experienced guide, you'll have no need to worry. Thanks to the low gravity, enough oxygen for twelve hours' normal working can be carried quite easily—and you'll never be away from shelter as long as that.

Don't attempt to imitate any of the locals you may see walking around without oxygen gear. They're second-generation colonists and are used to the low pressure. They can't breathe the Martian atmosphere any more than you can, but like the old-time native pearl divers they can make one lungful last for several minutes when necessary. Even so, it's a silly sort of trick and they're not supposed to do it.

As you know, the other great obstacle to life on Mars is the low temperature. The highest thermometer reading ever recorded is somewhere in the eighties, but that's quite exceptional. In the long winters, and during the night in summer *or* winter, it never rises above freezing. And I believe the record low is minus one hundred and ninety!

Well, you won't be outdoors at night, and for the sort of excursions you'll be doing, all that's needed is a simple thermosuit. It's very light, and traps the body heat so effectively that no other source of warmth is needed.

No doubt you'll want to see as much of Mars as you can during your stay. There are only two methods of transport outside the cities—sand fleas for short ranges and aircraft for longer distances. Don't misunderstand me when I say "short ranges"—a sand flea with a full charge of power cells is good for a couple of thousand miles, and it can do eighty miles an hour over good ground. Mars could never have been explored without them—you can *survey* a planet from space, but in the end someone with a pick and shovel has to do the dirty work filling in the map.

One thing that few visitors realize is just how big Mars is. Although it seems small beside the Earth, its land area is almost as great because so much of our planet is covered with oceans. So it's hardly surprising that there are vast regions that have never been properly explored—particularly around the poles. Those stubborn people who still believe that there was once an indigenous Martian civilization pin their hopes on these great blanks. Every so often you hear rumors of some wonderful archaeological discovery in the wastelands—but nothing ever comes of it.

Personally, I don't believe there ever *were* any Martians —but the planet is interesting enough for its own sake. You'll be fascinated by the plant life and the queer animals that manage to live without oxygen, migrating each year from hemisphere to hemisphere, across the ancient seabeds, to avoid the ferocious winter. The fight for survival on Mars has been fierce, and evolution has produced some pretty odd results. Don't go investigating any Martian life forms unless you have a guide, or you may get some unpleasant surprises.

Well, that's all I've got to say, except to wish you a pleasant trip. Oh, there *is* one other thing. My boy collects stamps, and I rather let him down when I was on Mars. If you could drop me a few letters while you're there—there's no need to put anything in them if you're too busy—I'd be much obliged. He's trying to collect a set of space-mail covers postmarked from each of the principle Martian cities, and if you could help—thanks a lot!

★ THE PLANETS ARE NOT ENOUGH
★

★ ALTOGETHER apart from its scientific value, space travel has one justification which transcends all others. It is probably the only way in which we can hope to answer one of the supreme questions of philosophy: Is Man alone in the Universe? It seems incredible that ours should be the only inhabited planet among the millions of worlds that must exist among the stars, but we cannot solve this problem by speculating about it. If it can be solved at all, it will be by visiting other planets to see for ourselves.

The Solar System, comprising the nine known worlds of our Sun and their numerous satellites, is a relatively compact structure, a snug little celestial oasis in an endless desert. It is true that millions of miles separate Earth from its neighbors, but such distances are cosmically trivial. They will even be trivial in terms of human engineering before another hundred years—a mere moment in historical time—have elapsed. However, the distances which sunder us from the possible worlds of other stars are of a totally different order of magnitude, and there are fundamental reasons for thinking that nothing—no scientific discovery or technical achievement—will ever make *them* trivial.

When today's chemical fuels have been developed to the ultimate, and such tricks as refueling in space have been fully exploited, we will have spaceships which can attain speeds of about ten miles a second. That means that the Moon will be reached in two or three days and the nearer planets in about half a year. (I am deliberately rounding these numbers off, and anyone who tries to check my arithmetic had better remember that spaceships will never travel in straight lines or at uniform speeds.) The remoter planets, such as Jupiter and Saturn, could be reached only after many years of travel, and so the trio Moon-Mars-Venus marks the practical limit of exploration for chemically propelled spaceships. Even for these cases, it is all too easy to demonstrate that hundreds of tons of fuel would be needed for each ton of payload that would make the round trip.

This situation, which used to depress the pre-atomic-energy astronauts, will not last for long. Since we are not concerned here with engineering details, we can take it for granted that eventually nuclear power, in some form or other, will be harnessed for the purposes of space flight. With energies a millionfold greater than those available from chemical fuels, speeds of hundreds, and ultimately thousands, of miles a second will be attainable. Against such speeds, the Solar System will shrink until the inner planets are no more than a few hours apart, and even Pluto will be only a week or two from Earth. Moreover, there should be no reasonable limit to the amount of equipment and material that could be taken on an interplanetary expedition. Anyone who doubts this may ponder the fact that the energy released by a single H-bomb is sufficient to carry about a million tons to Mars. It is true that we cannot as yet tap even a fraction of that energy for such a purpose, but there are already hints of how this may be done.

The short-lived Uranium Age will see the dawn of space flight; the succeeding era of fusion power will witness its fulfillment. But even when we can travel among the planets as freely as we now travel over this Earth, it seems that we will be no nearer to solving the problem of Man's place in the Universe. That is a secret that will still lie hidden in the stars.

All the evidence indicates that we are alone in the Solar System. True, there is almost certainly some kind of life on Mars, and possibly on Venus—perhaps even on the Moon. (The slight evidence for lunar vegetation comes from the amateur observers who actually *look* at the Moon, and is regarded skeptically by professional astronomers, who could hardly care less about a small slag heap little more than a light-second away.) Vegetation, however, can provide little intellectual companionship. Mars may be a paradise for the botanist, but it may have little to interest the zoologist—and nothing at all to lure the anthropologist and his colleagues across some scores of millions of miles of space.

This is likely to disappoint a great many people and to take much of the zest out of space travel. Yet it would be unreasonable to expect anything else; the planets have been in existence for several billion years, and only during the last .0001 per cent of that time has the human race been slightly civilized. Even if Mars and Venus have been (or will be) suitable for higher forms of life, the chances are wildly against our encountering beings anywhere near our cultural or intellectual level at this particular moment of time. If rational creatures exist on the planets, they will be millions of years behind us. We may expect to meet apes or angels, but never men.

The angels can probably be ruled out at once. If they existed, then surely they would already have come here to have a look at us. Some people, of course, think that this is just what they are doing. I can only say that they are going about it in a very odd manner.

We had better assume, therefore, that neither on Mars nor Venus, nor on any other of the planets, will explorers from Earth encounter intelligent life. We are the only castaways upon the tiny raft of the Solar System, as it drifts forever along the Gulf Streams of the Galaxy.

This, then, is the challenge that sooner or later the human spirit must face, when the planets have been conquered and all their secrets brought home to Earth. The nearest of the stars is a million times farther away than the closest of the planets. The spaceships we may expect to see a generation from now would take about a hundred thousand years to reach Proxima Centauri, our nearest stellar neighbor. Even the hypothetical nuclear-powered spaceships which a full century of atomic engineering may produce could hardly make the journey in less than a thousand years.

The expressive term "God's quarantine regulations" has been used to describe this state of affairs. At first sight, it appears that they are rigorously enforced. There may be millions of inhabited worlds circling other suns, harboring beings who to us would seem godlike, with civilizations and cultures beyond our wildest dreams. But we shall never meet them, and they for their part will never know of our existence.

So run the conclusions of most astronomers, even those who are quite convinced that mere common or garden interplanetary flight is just around the corner. But it is always dangerous to make negative predictions, and though the difficulties of *interstellar* travel are stupendous, they are not insuperable. It is by no means certain that Man must remain trapped in the Solar System for eternity, never to know if he is a lonely freak of no cosmic significance.

There are two ways in which we might gain direct knowledge of other stellar systems without ever leaving our own. Rather surprisingly, it can be shown that radio communication would be perfectly feasible across interstellar space, if very slow speed telegraphy were employed. However, we can hardly assume that anyone would be listening in at the precise frequency with a receiver tuned to the extremely narrow band which would have to be employed. And even if they were, it would be extremely tedious learning to talk to them with no initial knowledge of their language—and having to wait many years for any acknowledgment of our signals, as the radio waves came limping back across the light-years. If we sent a question to Proxima Centauri, it would be almost nine years before any answer could reach Earth.

A more practical, though at first sight more startling, solution would be to send a survey ship—unmanned. This would be a gigantic extrapolation of existing techniques, but it would not involve anything fundamentally new. Imagine an automatic vessel, crammed with every type of recording instrument and controlled by an electronic brain with preset instructions. It would be launched out across space aimed at a target it might not reach for a thousand years. But at last one of the stars ahead would begin to dominate the sky, and a century or so later, it would have grown into a sun, perhaps with planets circling round it. Sleeping instruments would wake to life, the tiny ship would check its speed, and its sense organs would start to record their impressions. It would circle world after world, following a program set up to cover all possible contingencies by men who had died a thousand years before. Then, with the priceless knowledge it had gained, it would begin the long voyage home.

This type of proxy exploration of the universe would be slow and uncertain, and would demand long-range planning beyond the capacity of our age. Yet if there is no other way of contacting the stars, this is how it might be done. One millennium would make the investment in technical skill so that the next would reap the benefit. It would be as if Archimedes were to start a research project which could produce no results before the time of Einstein.

If men, and not merely their machines, are ever to reach the planets of other suns, problems of much greater difficulty will have to be solved. Stated in its simplest form, the question is this: How can men survive a journey which may last for several thousand years? It is rather surprising to find that there are at least five different answers which must be regarded as theoretical possibilities—however far they may be beyond the scope of today's science.

Medicine may provide two rather obvious solutions. There appears to be no fundamental reason why men should die when they do. It is certainly not a matter of the body "wearing out" in the sense that an inanimate piece of machinery does, for in the course of a single year almost the entire fabric of the body is replaced by new material. When we have discovered the details of this process, it may be possible to extend the life span indefinitely if so desired. Whether a crew of immortals, however well-balanced and psychologically adjusted, could tolerate each other's company for several centuries in rather cramped quarters is an interesting subject for speculation.

Perhaps a better answer is that suggested by the story of Rip Van Winkle. Suspended animation (or, more accurately, a drastic slowing down of the body's metabolism) for periods of a few hours is now, of course, a medical commonplace. It requires no great stretch of the imagination to suppose that, with the aid of low temperatures and drugs, men may be able to hibernate for virtually unlimited periods. We can picture an automatic ship with its oblivious crew making the long journey across the interstellar night until, when a new sun was looming up, the signal was sent out to trigger the mechanisms which would revive the sleepers. When their survey was completed, they would head back to Earth and slumber again until the time came to awake once more, and to greet a world which would regard them as survivors from the distant past.

The third solution was, to the best of my knowledge, suggested over thirty years ago by Professor J. D. Bernal in a long out-of-print essay, *The World, the Flesh, and the Devil*, which must rank as one of the most outstanding feats of scientific imagination in literature. Even today, many of the ideas propounded in this little book have never been fully developed, either in or out of science fiction. (Any requests from fellow authors to borrow my copy will be flatly ignored.)

Bernal imagined entire societies launched across space, in gigantic arks which would be closed, ecologically balanced systems. They would, in fact, be miniature planets, upon which generations of men would live and die so that one day their remote descendants would return to Earth with the record of their celestial Odyssey.

The engineering, biological and sociological problems involved in such an enterprise would be of fascinating complexity. The artificial planets (at least several miles in diameter) would have to be completely self-contained and self-supporting, and no material of any kind could be wasted. Commenting on the implications of such closed systems, *Time* magazine's able, erudite science editor Jonathan Leonard once hinted that cannibalism would be compulsory among interstellar travelers. This would be a matter of definition; we crew members of the two-billion-man spaceship Earth do not consider ourselves cannibals, despite the fact that every one of us must have absorbed atoms which once formed part of Caesar and Socrates, Shakespeare and Solomon.

One cannot help feeling that the interstellar ark on its thousand-year voyages would be a cumbersome way of solving the problem, even if all the social and psychological difficulties could be overcome. (Would the fiftieth generation still share the aspirations of their Pilgrim Fathers who set out from Earth so long ago?) There are, however, more sophisticated ways of getting men to the stars than the crude, brute-force methods outlined above. After the hard-headed engineering of the last few paragraphs, what follows may appear to verge upon fantasy. It involves, in the most fundamental sense of the word, the storage of human beings. And by that I do not mean anything as naïve as suspended animation.

A few months ago, in an Australian laboratory, I was watching what appeared to be perfectly normal spermatozoa wriggling across the microscope field. They *were* perfectly normal, but their history was not. For three years, they had been utterly immobile in a deep freeze, and there seemed little doubt that they could be kept fertile for centuries by the same technique. What was still more surprising, there had been enough successes with the far larger and more delicate ova to indicate that they too might survive the same treatment. If this proves to be the case, reproduction will eventually become independent of time.

The social implications of this make anything in *Brave New World* seem like child's play, but I am not concerned here with the interesting results which might have been obtained by, for example, uniting the genes of Cleopatra and Newton, had this technique been available earlier in history. (When such experiments are started, however, it would be as well to remember Shaw's famous rejection of a similar proposal: "But suppose, my dear, it turns out to have my beauty and your brains?")*

The cumbersome interstellar ark, with its generations of travelers doomed to spend their entire lives in empty space,

---

* We have Shaw's word for it that the would-be geneticist was a complete stranger and not, as frequently stated, Isadora Duncan.

was merely a device to carry germ cells, knowledge and culture from one sun to another. How much more efficient to send only the cells, to fertilize them automatically some twenty years before the voyage was due to end, to carry the embryos through to birth by techniques already foreshadowed in today's biology labs, and to bring up the babies under the tutelage of cybernetic nurses who would teach them their inheritance and their destiny when they were capable of understanding it.

These children, knowing no parents, or indeed anyone of a different age from themselves, would grow up in the strange artificial world of their speeding ship, reaching maturity in time to explore the planets ahead of them—perhaps to be the ambassadors of humanity among alien races, or perhaps to find, too late, that there was no home for them there. If their mission succeeded, it would be their duty (or that of their descendants, if the first generation could not compete the task) to see that the knowledge they had gained was someday carried back to Earth.

Would any society be morally justified, we may well ask, in planning so onerous and uncertain a future for its unborn —indeed unconceived—children? That is a question which different ages may answer in different ways. What to one era would seem a cold-blooded sacrifice might to another appear a great and glorious adventure. There are complex problems here which cannot be settled by instinctive, emotional answers.

So far, we have assumed that all interstellar voyages must of necessity last for many hundreds or even thousands of years. The nearest star is more than four light-years away; the Galaxy itself—the island Universe of which our Sun is one insignificant member—is hundreds of thousands of light-years across; and the distances *between* the galaxies are of the order of a million light-years. The speed of light appears to be a fundamental limit to velocity; in this sense it is quite different from the now outmoded "sound barrier," which is merely an attribute of the particular gases which happen to constitute our atmosphere.

Even if we could reach the speed of light, therefore, interstellar journeys would still require many years of travel, and only in the case of the very nearest stars would it appear possible for a voyager to make the round trip in a single lifetime, without resort to such techniques as suspended animation. However, as we shall see, the actual situation is a good deal more complex than this.

First of all, is it even theoretically possible to build spaceships capable of approaching the speed of light? (That is, 186,000 miles a second or 670,000,000 m.p.h.) The problem is that of finding a sufficient source of energy and applying it. Einstein's famous equation $E = mc^2$ gives an answer—on paper—which a few centuries of technology may be able to realize in terms of engineering. If we can achieve the *total* annihilation of matter—not the conversion of a mere fraction of a per cent of it into energy—we can approach as near to the speed of light as we please. We can never reach it, but a journey at 99.9 per cent of the speed of light would, after all, take very little longer than one at exactly the speed of light, so the difference would hardly seem of practical importance.

Complete annihilation of matter is still as much a dream as atomic energy itself was twenty years ago. However, the discovery of the anti-proton (which engages in mutual suicide on meeting a normal proton) may be the first step on the road to its realization.

Traveling at speeds approaching that of light, however, involves us at once in one of the most baffling paradoxes which spring from the theory of relativity—the so-called "time dilation effect." It is impossible to explain *why* this effect occurs without delving into very elementary yet extremely subtle mathematics. (There is nothing difficult about basic relativity math: most of it is simple algebra. The difficulty lies in the underlying concepts.) Nevertheless, even if the explanation must be skipped, the results of the time-dilation effect can be stated readily enough in nontechnical language.

Time itself is a variable quantity; the rate at which it flows depends upon the speed of the observer. The difference is infinitesimal at the velocities of everyday life, and even at the velocities of normal astronomical bodies. It is all-important as we approach to within a few per cent of the speed of light. To put it crudely, the faster one travels, the more slowly time will pass. At the speed of light, time would cease to exist; the moment "Now" would last forever.

Let us take an extreme example to show what this implies. If a spaceship left Earth for Proxima Centauri at the speed of light, and came back at once at the same velocity, it would have been gone for some eight and one half years according to all the clocks and calendars of Earth. *But the people in the ship, and all their clocks, would have recorded no lapsed time at all.*

At a physically attainable speed, say ninety-five per cent of the velocity of light, the inhabitants of the ship would think that the round trip had lasted about three years. At ninety-nine per cent, it would have seemed little more than a year to them. In each case, however, they would return more than eight years—Earth time—after they had departed. (No allowance has been made here for stopping and starting, which would require additional time.)

If we imagine a more extensive trip, we get still more surprising results. The travelers might be gone for a thousand years, from the point of view of Earth, having set out for a star five hundred light-years away. If their ship had averaged 99.9 per cent of the speed of light, they would be fifty years older when they returned to an Earth—*where ten centuries had passed away!**

It should be emphasized that this effect, incredible though it appears to be, is one of the natural consequences of Einstein's theory. The equation connecting mass and energy once appeared to be equally fantastic and remote from any practical application. It would be very unwise, therefore, to assume that the equation linking time and velocity will never be of more than theoretical interest. Anything which does not violate natural laws must be considered a possibility—and the events of the last few decades have shown clearly enough that things which are possible will always be achieved if the incentive is sufficiently great.

Whether the incentive will be sufficient here is a question which only the future can answer. The men of five hundred or a thousand years from now will have motivations very different from ours, but if they are men at all they will still burn with that restless curiosity which has driven us over this world and which is about to take us into space. Sooner

---

* The physical reality of the time dilation effect has been the subject of unusually acrimonious debate in recent years. Very few scientists now have any doubt of its existence, but its magnitude may not have the values quoted above. My figures are based on Special Relativity, which is too unsophisticated to deal with the complexities of an actual flight.

or later we will come to the edge of the Solar System and will be looking out across the ultimate abyss. Then we must choose whether we reach the stars—or whether we wait until the stars reach us.

★ METEORS
★

★ IF you go out of doors on a clear, moonless night and look up at the sky, you will seldom have to wait for more than a few minutes before you see a meteor slide through the stars. These faint streaks of light, vanishing almost as soon as born, were a complete mystery to mankind for thousands of years. Until quite recent times, indeed, it was not even realized that they had any connection with the other heavenly bodies; they were considered to be purely atmospheric phenomena, perhaps something akin to lightning. The very word "meteor," with its obvious kinship to "meteorology," is a survival of this ancient belief.

Ours is an age in which subjects which once seemed of no interest to anyone except a few ivory-tower scientists have suddenly become of overwhelming practical (and, alas, all too often military) importance. So it is with the transient lines of fire in the night sky. Within the last few years, the study of meteors has become the concern of research teams all over the world; and tomorrow it may determine the very survival of great nations.

The fact that meteor trails are caused by fragments of matter from outer space entering the Earth's atmosphere at enormous velocities is now known to almost everybody. Yet it was not until the beginning of the last century that astronomers accepted this fact, and then only after a determined rear-guard action. Science (if there is such a thing as Science with a capital S!) is often accused of being orthodox and unwilling to give heed to new ideas, and there are times when the charge has some truth in it. The argument over the origin of meteors provides a perfect example of this.

Though there had been reports in all times and from all lands of stones falling from the sky, the scientists of the French Academy, in the closing years of the eighteenth century—when it was confidently believed that the Age of Reason had dawned—dismissed all such tales as superstitious nonsense. They reacted, in fact, much as an astronomer of today would do when confronted with a typical flying saucer report—though it by no means follows that the sequel will be similar. And then, in 1803, almost as if Nature had determined to teach the skeptical scientists a lesson, a great shower of meteoric stones fell in Normandy— geographically speaking, on the Academy's doorstep. Thereafter no one doubted the fact that objects from outer space entered the Earth's atmosphere and occasionally reached the surface.

It was another thirty years before meteors attracted much further attention; then they did so with a spectacle the like of which has seldom been matched before or since. Listen to the words of a South Carolina planter, describing what happened on the night of November 11, 1833:

I was suddenly awakened by the most distressing cries that ever fell on my ears. Shrieks of horror and cries of mercy I could hear from most of the negroes of the three plantations. . . . While earnestly listening for the cause I heard a faint voice near the door, calling my name. I arose and, taking my sword, stood at the door. At this moment I heard the same voice still beseeching me to rise and saying, "Oh my God, the world is on fire!" I then opened the door, and it is difficult to say which excited me most—the awfulness of the scene, or the distressing cries of the negroes. Upwards of a hundred lay prostrate on the ground, some speechless, and some with the bitterest cries, but with their hands raised, imploring God to save the world and them. The scene was truly awful: for never did rain fall much thicker than the meteors fell towards the Earth: East, West, North and South it was the same.

Such was the great shower of 1833, which dramatically demonstrated that meteors could occur not only as sporadic wanderers but also in enormous clusters or streams. As a result of many years of observation, large numbers of these meteor showers have been identified and their dates of arrival noted. For example, around the twelfth of August every year, meteors will be seen streaking from the heart of the constellation Perseus at the rate of about one a minute. And between the fourteenth and sixteenth of November, in the constellation of Leo, the shower which caused such alarm over the southern states in 1833 still puts on an annual display—though in most years it is so feeble that one would never notice it unless one was on the lookout.

Until the close of the Second World War, the study of meteors was a somewhat neglected branch of astronomy. Since they are so transient and unpredictable, they cannot be watched through telescopes—except by pure chance—and hence almost all observations until recently were naked-eye ones made by amateur astronomers with no equipment but a notebook, a watch, a thorough knowledge of the constellations, unlimited patience and a complete indiffe ᵣ ᵤ ce to cold and fatigue. These devoted souls would spend their nights watching the stars, and every time a meteor flashed across the sky would note its duration and would pinpoint the beginning and end of its track. It may seem surprising, to those who think that astronomers have to work with huge and expensive instruments, that anything useful could be discovered by such simple means. Yet it was from thousands of such naked-eye observations that almost all our knowledge of meteors was derived, until the invention of radar gave astronomy a new and unexpected weapon of tremendous power.

Behind this there is a story of war and science that is still largely untold. During the late thirties, Britain began to build the chain of radar stations without which the Royal Air Force could never had held the *Luftwaffe* at bay. The men who designed and constructed the three-hundred-foot-high towers along the east coast of England changed the history of the world, by defeating Goering's bombers in the Battle of Britain. Three years later, in 1944, they were called upon again to fight the weapon which made those bombers obsolete.

The V2 rocket which the radar chain now had to detect traveled ten times as fast as any bomber, and twenty times as high. Nevertheless, the hastily modified radar picked them up. It also picked up something else—something that produced strange echoes seventy or eighty miles above the earth.

These echoes, it was soon discovered, were due to meteors — or, to be more accurate, to the trails of intensely heated gas which meteors leave in their wake as they plunge into the upper atmosphere at speeds often exceeding 100,000 miles an hour. It was obviously a matter of great importance to distinguish between the echoes caused by meteors and those produced by rockets. And it is even more important now that those rockets can carry a million tons of explosive power instead of the miserable one ton of the quaint, old-fashioned V2. . . .

After the war, when radar apparatus was available for more peaceful uses, a regular watch was kept for meteors at "radio observatories" throughout the world. The enormous advantage of radar for this work lies in the fact that it is independent of weather conditions and can operate just as well during daylight as at night. Previously, there had been no way of observing meteors except after darkness—and even then only when there was no Moon to flood the sky with light.

It is hardly surprising, therefore, that some remarkable discoveries were very quickly made. The most spectacular of these was undoubtedly the detection, by the group of radio astronomers at Manchester, England, of great meteor showers that occur during the hours of daylight and so are quite invisible to the eye. Every summer, showers take place which if they occurred after nightfall would produce a display almost as dramatic as the one in 1833. Between June and August, vast belts of meteors are sweeping unseen, and until today unsuspected, across the daylight skies of Earth.

Continuous watches are now being kept by automatic equipment which, as soon as a meteor is located, photographs its radar echo on a cathode-ray tube. From this it is possible to calculate the meteor's height and velocity, and thus the orbit it was following through space before it met its doom. This radar watch has already settled one question concerning which astronomers had been fighting furiously for more than a generation.

One school of thought maintained that a substantial proportion of meteors did not belong to the Solar System at all, but came from interstellar space—that there were, in other words, vast streams of meteoric matter flowing between the stars. The evidence of this startling theory was quite strong—indeed, at first sight overwhelming. When the velocities of meteors were measured by the indirect methods which were the only ones available before radar, many were found to be traveling so fast that they could not possibly be revolving around the Sun. In the Earth's neighborhood, any object moving at more than 94,000 miles an hour could only be a visitor to the Solar System, not a permanent resident. This is the limiting speed above which the Sun can no longer keep a body under its gravitational control. Anything moving faster than this, accordingly, must have fallen into the Solar System from outside—and would shoot out of it again after doing a tight turn around the Sun.

The more accurate radar methods proved conclusively that meteors traveling faster than this solar speed limit did not exist; all meteors, therefore, are as much captives of the Sun as are Earth and other planets, and revolve around it in similar closed orbits.

Although meteors do not travel faster than 94,000 miles an hour with respect to the Sun in our part of the Solar System, the velocities with which they hit our atmosphere can be far higher than this, since the Earth itself is racing along its orbit at 66,000 miles an hour. When Earth and meteor hit head on, therefore, their combined speed may be as much as 160,000 miles an hour—a velocity which would take one to the Moon in ninety minutes.

On the other hand, when a meteor catches up to the Earth from the rear its speed of approach is relatively low, and this sometimes produces a remarkable effect. Though most meteor trails flash out and vanish in a second, when one of these "slow" meteors enters the atmosphere it may make a sedate and dignified—not to say impressive—progress across the sky. There have even been occasions when an entire procession of meteors has put on such a display, apparently for the express purpose of adding to the flying-saucer mythos. (I'm sorry to raise that subject again, but it's never far away where meteors are concerned.)

It is very important to draw a clear distinction between meteors themselves and the trails they produce in the sky when they happen to hit the Earth's atmosphere. It is these trails that are observed both by the eye and by the electronic senses of the radar telescope; the meteors are far too small to be detected. There is a close analogy here with something we have all witnessed when a jet plane passes high overhead. Often the vapor trail can be seen stretching for miles across the deep blue of the atmosphere—but of the plane itself there is no sign.

In the case of meteors, the disparity between the size of the trail and the object causing it is far more extreme. Even a very bright meteor—one producing a burst of light outshining all the stars put together—is only about half in inch in diameter. Such a giant is quite rare; perhaps a thousand hit the entire Earth every hour. Anyone who considers that this makes them hardly uncommon should remember that the Earth is a rather large object, and that in an hour it carves out a tunnel through space 8,000 miles in diameter and 66,000 miles long.

The total number of meteors, of *all* sizes, that hit the Earth every hour is enormous—probably in the billions. But the vast majority of these are smaller than grains of sand; most, indeed, are specks of dust that would be invisible to the naked eye.

Ever since space travel and artificial satellites began to be considered seriously, a good deal of attention has been paid to the possible hazard that meteors might represent. As long ago as 1946 the Rand Corporation concerned itself with this problem on behalf of the Air Force, and made p____ its findings in an unclassified report. The results were re____ ing and have since been confirmed by satellite observations meteors are very much less of a danger to space travelers than automobiles are to practically everybody. You would die of old age on an interplanetary journey before you met a meteor large enough to do any serious damage—though it is possible that there may be enough meteoric dust around in space to "sandblast" windows and optical surfaces after a few years of continuous operations. Meteors may be a nuisance, but they will certainly not be a menace.

About ten times a day the Earth encounters a meteor which is sufficiently large not to be consumed by the friction of its passage through the atmosphere, and which manages to reach the surface intact. It is then termed a meteorite, passing from the jurisdiction of astronomy to that of meteoritics (studied, heaven help them, by meteoriticists. Try to say that quickly after the fourth or fifth martini). Since these falling bodies are the only samples we have of matter from outside the Earth, they are of great interest to science and nowadays any report of a falling meteorite sparks off something like a gold rush.

The average meteorite is an unprepossessing lump of stone or nickel-iron which looks as if it had been picked up from a slag heap. In a sense, indeed, it is a lump of cosmic slag—possibly part of the debris left over when the planets were formed, at least five billion years ago. Once or twice every century, really large meteorites hit the Earth; it happened in Siberia in 1908 and again in 1947. Several hundred tons of iron and stone plunging down through the atmosphere at ten or more times the speed of an artillery shell can produce a blast wave greater than that of an atomic bomb; the 1908 meteorite felled a forest, snapping off tree trunks for miles around so that they lay like matchsticks pointing away from the impact area.

During the course of geological time, there must have been thousands of such collisions, but the effect of weather and vegetation have obliterated the evidence—and it should also be remembered that most meteorites must come down in the sea. Until recently, the famous Meteor Crater in Arizona was the largest-known survival of one of these prehistoric catastrophes; with a diameter of over four thousand feet, it is a very impressive object, especially from the air.

During the war, United States and Canadian Air Force pilots noticed a curious circular lake in the frozen wastes of Northern Quebec, and this has now been found to mark the site of a meteor crater more than eleven thousand feet in diameter. The Ungava Crater, as it has been named, has certainly been there for many thousands of years, for the glaciers of the last Ice Age have ground their way across it and retreated again, leaving unmistakable marks of their passage. So, though the Ungava Crater is more than twice as large as its Arizona rival, it is not in the same pristine condition and much of the evidence of its formation has probably been erased.

There is little doubt that air surveys will reveal many more formations of this type, some of them in populated areas. At the village of Cabrerolles in Southern France, for instance, lies a group of craters which no one had ever noticed because they had been completely overgrown with vegetation—one of them, indeed, is occupied by a vineyard. It is not yet certain that they were caused by meteorites, and anyone who knows much about the French peasantry will realize the scientists may have to do some hard bargaining before they can start digging for nickel-iron fragments.

It is always possible that a large meteorite may fall on a city—and one can guess the consequences if, by doubly bad luck, this should happen during a period of international tension. In the whole of recorded history, however, there are less than half a dozen cases of deaths from falling meteorites, and a recent statistical analysis showed that there is only about one chance in three that a single member of the human race will be hit by a meteorite during the entire twentieth century. An insurance company wishing to make headlines, therefore, would not be taking much of a risk if it offered ten billion dollars compensation to any client meeting this unusual mishap. If the phrase "almost unique" can be justified in strict logic, here is a case for employing it.*

Yet, though the chance of a personal encounter with a meteorite is so remote, these visitors from outer space now affect the lives of every one of us. Today, the problem which first confronted the British radar experts during the closing months of the war has become of vital importance. How is one to distinguish between an intercontinental ballistic missile and a meteor which may be traveling at the same speed and at the same height? A few minutes' wait will give the answer, of course; but then it may be a little too late.

There is considerable evidence that without meteors we would have no long-range radio communication. The only way that radio waves can get round the curve of the Earth is by bouncing off the ionized layers in the upper atmosphere, some seventy miles above our heads. Why the air in this region should act as a kind of radio mirror is still some-

---

* Despite the statistics, this incredible event occurred almost at the time these words were written. In December, 1954, Mrs. Hewlitt Hodges of Sylacauga, Alabama, was grazed by a ten-pound meteorite that came through the roof of her house!

The first, and probably only, case of a meteorite hitting an automobile also occurred in the United States at Benld, Illinois, in September, 1938.

thing of a mystery; during the daytime, it is true, the Sun's rays are able to keep it electrically charged, but that does not explain how it persists at night. It is now fairly certain that the continuous gentle rain of meteor dust from space is responsible for at least one of the electrified layers which enable us to send our voices round the world.

Some recent research, started in Australia, has shown that meteors may, after all, have some association with meteorology. The link is a most unexpected one but if it can be established will be of very great practical importance. It appears that our small-scale attempts to produce rain by "seeding" clouds with dry ice and other substances have been anticipated by Nature; the ceaseless shower of meteoric dust filtering down from the stars may have the same effect. Long-range weather prediction, therefore, will have to take account of the meteor streams which the Earth encounters in its passage through space.

It would be hard to find a better example of the way in which apparently unrelated branches of science prove to be closely connected. Though the laws which govern the Universe may be simple, the effects which they produce can be exceedingly complex. One of the giant planets may deflect a meteor stream half a billion miles from Earth, so that ages later our world encounters an abnormally high concentration of dust as it sweeps along its orbit. And so an event far off in space and time can cause rains and floods which may destroy many lives and undo the work of generations of men.

A hundred years ago the greatest poet of the Victorian Age wrote these words:

> Now sleeps the crimson petal, now the white;
> Nor waves the cypress in the palace walk;
> Nor winks the gold fin in the porphyry font
> The fire-fly wakens; waken thou with me.
>
> Now droops the milkwhite peacock like a ghost,
> And like a ghost she glimmers on to me.
> Now lies the Earth all Danaë to the stars,
> And all thy heart lies open unto me.
>
> Now slides the silent meteor on, and leaves
> A shining furrow, as thy thoughts in me.

A different description, perhaps, from the one that science gives, and perhaps some may prefer it. Yet both are equally valid—and why should we not appreciate the beauty of that "shining furrow" all the more, now that we are beginning to uncover its secret?

Where is he that is born King of the Jews? for we have seen his star in the east, and are come to worship him.

★ **THE STAR OF THE MAGI**
★

★ Go out of doors any morning this December,* and look up at the eastern sky an hour or so before dawn. You will see there one of the most beautiful sights in all the heavens—a blazing, blue-white beacon, many times brighter than Sirius, the most brilliant of the stars. Apart from the Moon itself, it will be the brightest object you will ever see in the night sky. It will still be visible even when the Sun rises; indeed, you will be able to find it at midday if you know exactly where to look.

It is the planet Venus, our sister world, reflecting across the gulfs of space the sunlight glancing from her unbroken cloud shield. Every nineteen months she appears in the morning sky, rising shortly before the Sun, and all who see this brilliant herald of the Christmas dawn will inevitably be reminded of the star that led the Magi to Bethlehem.

What was that star, assuming that it had some natural explanation? Could it, in fact, have been Venus? At least one book has been written to prove this theory, but it will not stand up to serious examination. To all the peoples of the Eastern world, Venus was one of the most familiar objects in the sky. Even today, she serves as a kind of alarm clock to the Arab nomads. When she rises, it is time to start

---

* This article was written to appear in December, 1954, but as the statement is correct for approximately one Christmas in three, I have left the opening unchanged.

moving, to make as much progress as possible before the Sun begins to blast the desert with its heat. For thousands of years, shining more brilliantly than we ever see her in our cloudy northern skies, she has watched the camps struck and the caravans begin to move.

Even to the ordinary, uneducated Jews of Herod's kingdom, there could have been nothing in the least remarkable about Venus. And the Magi were no ordinary men; they were certainly experts on astronomy, and must have known the movements of the planets better than do ninety-nine people out of a hundred today. To explain the Star of Bethlehem we must look elsewhere.

The Bible gives us very few clues; all that we can do is to consider some possibilities which at this distance in time can be neither proved nor disproved. One of these possibilities—the most spectacular and awe-inspiring of all—has been discovered only in the last few years, but let us first look at some of the earlier theories.

In addition to Venus, there are four other planets visible to the naked eye—Mercury, Mars, Jupiter and Saturn. During their movements across the sky, two planets may sometimes appear to pass very close to one another—though in reality, of course, they are actually millions of miles apart.

Such occurrences are called "conjunctions"; on occasion they may be so close that the planets cannot be separated by the naked eye. This happened for Mars and Venus on October 4, 1953, when for a short while the two planets appeared to be fused together to give a single star. Such a spectacle is rare enough to be very striking, and the great astronomer Johannes Kepler devoted much time to proving that the Star of Bethlehem was a special conjunction of Jupiter and Saturn. The planets passed very close together (once again, remember, this was purely from the Earth's point of view—in reality they were half a billion miles apart!) in May, 7 B.C. This is quite near the date of Christ's birth, which probably took place in the spring of 7 or 6 B.C. (This still surprises most people, but as Herod is known to have died early in 4 B.C., Christ must have been born before 5 B.C. We should add six years to the calendar for A.D. to mean what it says.)

Kepler's proposal, however, is as unconvincing as the Venus theory. Better calculations than those he was able to make in the seventeenth century have shown that this particular conjunction was not a very close one, and the planets were always far enough apart to be easily separated by the eye. Moreover, there was a closer conjunction in 66 B.C., which on Kepler's theory should have brought a delegation of wise men to Bethlehem sixty years too soon!

In any case, the Magi could be expected to be as familiar with such events as with all other planetary movements, and the Biblical account also indicates that the Star of Bethlehem was visible over a period of weeks (it must have taken the Magi a considerable time to reach Judea, have their interview with Herod and then go on to Bethlehem). The conjunction of two planets lasts only a very few days, since they soon separate in the sky and go once more upon their individual ways.

We can get over the difficulty if we assume that the Magi were astrologers ("Magi" and "magician" have a common root) and had somehow deduced the birth of the Messiah from a particular configuration of the planets, which to them, if to no one else, had a unique significance. It is an interesting fact that the Jupiter-Saturn conjunction of 7 B.C. occurred in the constellation Pisces, the Fish. Now though the ancient Jews were too sensible to believe in astrology, the constellation Pisces was supposed to be connected with them. Anything peculiar happening in Pisces would, naturally, direct the attention of Oriental astrologers toward Jerusalem.*

This theory is simple and plausible, but a little disappointing. One would like to think that the Star of Bethlehem was something more dramatic, and not anything to do with the familiar planets whose behavior had been perfectly well known for thousands of years before the birth of Christ. Of course, if one accepts as *literally* true the statement that "the star, which they saw in the east, *went before them, till*

---

* Since writing the above, I have come across a most informative little brochure, "The Star of Bethlehem," by Roy K. Marshall, available from the American Museum's Hayden Planetarium (and doubtless from other planetariums elsewhere). Dr. Marshall discusses at some length the actual date of the Nativity and points out that the Magi were probably Persian priests—followers of Zoroaster. He gives a very full account of the Saturn-Jupiter "triple conjunction" of 7 B.C., and adds the thought-provoking comment that the same phenomenon occurred in 1940 *and* 1941.

it came and stood over where the young Child was," no natural explanation is possible. Any heavenly body—star, planet, comet or whatever—must share in the normal movement of the sky, rising in the east and setting some hours later in the west. Only the Pole Star, because it lies on the invisible axis of the turning Earth, appears unmoving in the sky and can act as a fixed and constant guide.

But the phrase, "went before them," like so much else in the Bible, can be interpreted in many ways. It may be that the star—whatever it might have been—was so close to the Sun that it could be seen only for a short period near dawn, and so would never have been visible except in the eastern sky. Like Venus when she is a morning star, it might have risen shortly before the Sun, then been lost in the glare of the new day before it could climb very far up the sky. The wise men would thus have seen it ahead of them at the beginning of each day, and then lost it in the dawn before it had veered round to the south. Many other readings are equally possible.

Very well, then—can we discover some astronomical phenomenon, sufficiently startling to surprise men completely familiar with the movements of the stars and planets, which fits the Biblical text?

Let's see if a comet would answer the specification. There have been no really spectacular comets this century—though there were several in the eighteen hundreds—and most people do not know what they look like or how they behave. They even confuse them with meteors, which any observer is bound to see if he goes out on a clear night and watches the sky for half an hour.

No two classes of object could be more different. A meteor is a speck of matter, usually smaller than a grain of sand, which burns itself up by friction as it tears through the outer layers of Earth's atmosphere. But a comet may be millions of times larger than the entire Earth, and may dominate the night sky for weeks on end. A really great comet may look like a searchlight shining across the stars, and it is not surprising that such a portentous object always caused alarm when it appeared in the heavens. As Calpurnia said to Caesar:

When beggars die, there are no comets seen;
The heavens themselves blaze forth the death of princes.

Most comets have a bright, starlike core or nucleus, which is completely dwarfed by their enormous tail—a lunminous appendage which may be in the shape of a narrow beam or a broad, diffuse fan. At first sight it would seem very unlikely that anyone would call such an object a star, but as a matter of fact in old records comets are sometimes referred to, not inaptly, as "hairy stars."

Comets are unpredictable: the great ones appear without warning, come racing in through the planets, bank sharply round the Sun, and then head out toward the stars—not to be seen again for hundreds or even millions of years. Only a few large comets—such as Halley's—have relatively short periods and have been observed on many occasions. Halley's comet, which takes seventy-five years to go round its orbit, has managed to put in an appearance at several historic events. It was visible just before the sack of Jerusalem in A.D. 66, and before the Norman invasion of England in A.D. 1066. Of course, in ancient times (or modern ones, for that matter) it was never very difficult to find a suitable disaster to attribute to any given comet. It is not surprising, therefore, that their reputation as portents of evil lasted for so long.

It is perfectly possible that a comet appeared just before the birth of Christ. Attempts have been made, without success, to see if any of the known comets were visible around that date. (Halley's, as will be seen from the figures above, was just a few years too early on its appearance before the fall of Jerusalem.) But the number of comets whose paths and periods we do know is very small compared with the colossal number that undoubtedly exists. If a comet did shine over Bethlehem, it may not be seen again from Earth for a hundred thousand years.

We can picture it in that Oriental dawn—a band of light streaming up from the eastern horizon, perhaps stretching vertically toward the zenith. The tail of the comet always points away from the Sun; the comet would appear, therefore, like a great arrow, aimed at the east. As the Sun rose, it would fade into invisibility; but the next morning, it would be in almost the same place, still directing the travelers to their goal. It might be visible for weeks before it disappeared once more into the depths of space.

The picture is a dramatic and attractive one. It may even be the correct explanation; one day, perhaps, we shall know.

But there is yet another theory, and this is the one which most astronomers would probably accept today. It makes the other explanations look very trivial and commonplace indeed, for it leads us to contemplate one of the most astonishing—and terrifying—events yet discovered in the whole realm of Nature.

We will forget now about planets and comets and the other denizens of our own tight little Solar System. Let us go out across *real* space, right out to the stars—those other suns, many far greater than our own, which sheer distance has dwarfed to dimensionless points of light.

Most of the stars shine with unwavering brilliance, century after century. Sirius appears now exactly as it did to Moses, as it did to Neanderthal Man, as it did to the dinosaurs—if they ever bothered to look at the night sky. Its brilliance has changed little during the entire history of our Earth, and will be the same a billion years from now.

But there are some stars—the so-called "novae" or new stars—which through internal causes suddenly become celestial atomic bombs. Such a star may explode so violently that it leaps a hundred-thousand-fold in brilliance within a few hours. One night it may be invisible to the naked eye; on the next, it may dominate the sky. If our Sun became such a nova, Earth would melt to slag and puff into vapor in a matter of minutes, and only the outermost of the planets would survive.

Novae are not uncommon; many are observed every year, though few are near enough to be visible except through telescopes. They are the routine, everyday disasters of the Universe.

Two or three times in every thousand years, however, there occurs something which makes a mere nova about as inconspicuous as a firefly at noon. When a star becomes a *super*-nova, its brilliance may increase not by a hundred thousand but by a *billion* in the course of a few hours. The last time such an event was witnessed by human eyes was in A.D. 1604; there was another supernova in A.D. 1572 (so brilliant that it was visible in broad daylight); and the Chinese astronomers recorded one in A.D. 1054. It is quite possible that the Bethlehem star was such a supernova, and if so one can draw some very surprising conclusions.

We'll assume that Supernova Bethlehem was about as bright as the supernova of A.D. 1572—often called "Tycho's star," after the great astronomer who observed it at the time. Since this star could be seen by day, it must have been as brilliant as Venus. As we also know that a supernova is, in reality, at least a hundred million times more brilliant than our own Sun, a very simple calculation tells us how far away it must have been, for its *apparent* brightness to equal that of Venus.

It turns out that Supernova Bethlehem was more than three thousand light-years—or, if you prefer, 18,000,000,-000,000,000 miles—away. That means that its light had been traveling for at least three thousand years before it reached Earth and Bethlehem, so that the awesome cataclysm of which it was the symbol took place five thousand years ago, when the great pyramid was still fresh from the builders.

Let us, in imagination, cross the gulfs of space and time and go back to the moment of the catastrophe. We might find ourselves watching an ordinary star—a sun, perhaps, no different from our own. There may have been planets circling it; we do not know how common planets are in the scheme of the Universe, and how many suns have such small companions. But there is no reason to think that they are rare, and many novae must be the funeral pyres of worlds, and perhaps races, greater than ours.

There is no warning at all—only a steadily rising intensity of the sun's light. Within minutes the change is noticeable; within an hour, the nearer worlds are burning. The star is expanding like a balloon, blasting off shells of gas at a million miles an hour as it blows its outer layers into space. Within a day, it is shining with such supernal brilliance that it gives off more light than *all the other suns in the Universe combined*. If it had planets, they are now no more than flecks of flame in the still-expanding shells of fire. The conflagration will burn for weeks before the dying star collapses back into quiescence.

But let us consider what happens to the light of the

nova, which moves a thousand times more swiftly than the blast wave of the explosion. It will spread out into space, and after four or five years it will reach the next star. If there are planets circling that star, they will suddenly be illuminated by a second sun. It will give them no appreciable heat, but will be bright enough to banish night completely, for it will be more than a thousand times more luminous than our full Moon. All that light will come from a single blazing point, since even from its nearest neighbor Supernova Bethlehem would appear too small to show a disk.

Century after century, the shell of light will continue to expand around its source. It will flash past countless suns and flare briefly in the skies of their planets. Indeed, on the most conservative estimate, this great new star must have shone over thousands of worlds before its light reached Earth—and to all those worlds it appeared far, far brighter than it did to the men it led to Judea.

For as the shell of light expanded, it faded also. Remember, by the time it reached Bethlehem it was spread over the surface of a sphere six thousand light-years across. A thousand years earlier, when Homer was singing the song of Troy, the nova would have appeared twice as brilliant to any watchers further upstream, as it were, to the time and place of the explosion.

That is a strange thought; there is a stranger one to come. For the light of Supernova Bethlehem is still flooding out through space; it has left Earth far behind in the twenty centuries that have elapsed since men saw it for the first and last time. Now that light is spread over a sphere ten thousand light-years across, and must be correspondingly fainter. It is simple to calculate how bright the supernova must be to any beings who may be seeing it now as a new star in *their* skies. To them, it will still be far more brilliant than any other star in the entire heavens, for its brightness will have fallen only by 50 per cent on its extra two thousand years of travel.

At this very moment, therefore, the Star of Bethlehem may still be shining in the skies of countless worlds, circling far suns. Any watchers on those worlds will see its sudden appearance and its slow fading, just as the Magi did two thousand years ago when the expanding shell of light swept past the Earth. And for thousands of years to come, as its radiance ebbs out toward the frontiers of the Universe, Supernova Bethlehem will still have power to startle all who see it, wherever—and whatever—they may be.

Astronomy, as nothing else can do, teaches men humility. We know now that our Sun is merely one undistinguished member of a vast family of stars, and no longer think of ourselves as being at the center of creation. Yet it is strange to think that before its light fades away below the limits of vision, we may have shared the Star of Bethlehem with the beings of perhaps a million worlds—and that to many of them, nearer to the source of the explosion, it must have been a far more wonderful sight than ever it was to any human eyes.

What did they make of it—and did it bring them good tidings, or ill?

Postscript

Many planetariums put on a special display at Christmas in which the possible explanations of the Star of the Nativity are discussed and demonstrated. New York's Hayden Planetarium, for example, has a particularly impressive and moving program "The Christmas Sky" every December, which should not be missed by anyone who has an opportunity to see it.

★ WHERE'S EVERYBODY?

★ At this moment of time, when humanity stands upon the threshold of space and has already launched its first vehicles beyond the atmosphere, there is a centuries-old question which presses more and more urgently for an answer. In almost any astronomy book you will find a chapter devoted to the subject "Is There Life on Other

Worlds?"—the answer given depending upon the optimism of the author and the period in which he is writing (for there are fashions in astronomy as in everything else).

Today, that question needs to be reframed and brought up to date. There must be very few astronomers now who are conceited enough to suppose that only the Earth is the abode of life, or even that it is the only home of intelligence. Assuming this to be the case, we have an interesting problem on our hands. How are we to explain the peculiar behavior of the other intelligent races which share the Universe?

What peculiar behavior, Holmes? Assuming that such races exist, they have done absolutely nothing about us.

Precisely, my dear Watson.

Having stated the problem, let's look at it as scientifically and dispassionately as we ca. It falls into three distinct sections—astronomical, biologica¹ and technical, and we'll deal with them in that order.

On a clear, moonless night the sky seems so packed with stars that it is hard to believe that they could ever be counted. Yet in reality the unaided eye can see only a couple of thousand stars at any one time; even a small telescope shows millions, and the photographic plate billions. All those stars are suns, many of them larger than ours, most of them smaller. Unfortunately, there is no way in which we can tell if any of them possess planets, except in cases so unusual that only a couple of examples are known.

However, even these examples are enough to suggest that planets are not so rare as they were once thought to be; it may in fact turn out that most stars have small, cold bodies circling them. And if no more than one in a hundred does, that would still be some *billion* planetary systems in our Galaxy alone.

By the laws of probability, we should expect at least one planet capable of supporting life to exist within ten light-years of the Earth. (The nearest star, Proxima Centauri, is just over four light-years away; ten light-years is the approximate distance of the brightest star, Sirius.) On the cosmic scale, such distances are completely trivial. Our Galaxy—the island Universe of which the Sun is not a particularly outstanding member—is about a hundred thousand light-years from end to end. And the remotest of the

them. Which brings us back to our opening question: *If they are so advanced, why haven't they come here?*

At this point, I have to pause briefly to deal with the hordes of flying-saucer believers who have suddenly appeared on the horizon, waving affidavits and smudgy photographs. To dispose of them would need another article a good deal longer than this one, not all of it printable in a book intended for general circulation. So I'll merely state my views on this agitated subject, without giving the reasons that have led me to them after several years of thought, reading, interviewing and personal observations.* I think there may be "Unidentified Flying Objects" which are exactly what their name implies, and which may turn out to be quite interesting and exciting when we discover their cause. At the same time I am pretty sure that they're not, repeat, not, spaceships; if they were, so many consequences would have arisen which, in fact, have not done so. (The most obvious one—we and the Russians would be the best of friends.) If I'm wrong, that still proves the main point of my thesis, so I can't lose anyway.

Assuming, therefore, that during modern times there have been no visitors from space, we have to look for an explanation. It may well be argued (and indeed has been by many eminent scientists) that our apparent isolation can be explained very simply. Travel from planet to planet inside the Solar System may be possible in the relatively near future, so that we shall visit neighboring worlds such as Mars and Venus. But travel to the planets of other suns—*interstellar* travel—may be totally impossible because of the sheer distances involved. On this theory, the Universe may be full of intelligent races, but they must forever exist in total ignorance of each other, quarantined by space itself.

This is a serious and plausible argument, and must be dealt with before we proceed any further. First of all, let us get clearly into our minds the important—the fundamental —distinction between the distances of interplanetary space, which our children will be challenging, and the immensely greater distances which separate us from the stars.

Planetary distances are about a millionfold greater than those of ordinary, everyday life. (For example—Venus at

* I have given them in "Things in the Sky" (page 148).

its closest, 26 million miles; Mars at its closest, 35 million miles.) The stars, however, are about *a million times further away still* (e.g., Proixma Centauri, 25 million *million* miles.) When we get to the remotest planet, therefore, we will be little nearer the stars than we are today.

But distance itself means nothing; all that really matters is the length of time any particular journey requires. In the last hundred years we have seen the world shrink beyond the wildest imagination of our forefathers. Jules Verne was laughed at when he dared to suggest that one might circumnavigate the Earth in eighty days, but now it has been done in two—and the IGY satellites, the harbingers of the Space Age, go round the globe in almost as many minutes as Phileas Fogg required days.

This steady increase in speed shows no sign of slackening; indeed, in the last decade the development of the jet and the rocket has given the curve an even steeper upward trend. We already know how long the first interplanetary journeys will take, with the fuels and techniques that exist today. Mars and Venus are both much less than a year's flight away with chemical fuels; when *atomic* propulsion becomes available, a few decades from now, the journeys will be measured in weeks, and ultimately in days. This state of affairs will arise nearer the beginning of the next century than its end. It is partly because interplanetary travel must become possible quite early in the history of any technically minded race that I think it most unlikely that there is intelligent life elsewhere in the Solar System. It is much more likely that we have missed the Martians by a few million years, and that the Venusians may miss us by even more.

So we must look beyond the Sun's other planets for life—at least intelligent life, for there are good grounds for thinking that there is vegetation on Mars—and pin our hopes upon the distant stars. Can we—or any other race—ever hope to attain such velocities that the interstellar gulfs will be bridged in reasonably short periods of time?

I'll now go out on a limb by saying that this is one question that we *can* answer, even today. And the answer is "Yes, but—"

To put the matter in the right perspective, let's look at the entire gamut of speed, past, present and future. The past can be dealt with very briefly; from the dawn of history until the beginning of the nineteenth century, no man had ever traveled much faster than ten miles an hour.

There are men still alive who can remember when 100 m.p.h. was reached; yet 1,000 m.p.m. was attained—and doubled—during the last decade. Manned flight at 10,000 m.p.h. will be achieved in the 1960's; unmanned rockets have already passed this speed, and the satellites and space probes far exceed it.

You'll notice that we are going up in steps of ten. Each jump seemed enormous when it was made—and nothing much to boast about when it had become history. The next surge forward—to 100,000 m.p.h.—will take place when atomic energy is harnessed to rocket propulsion, and today's chemical fuels join the wax candles and kerosene lamps in the museums. (This may be sooner than we think. Almost every aviation company is now working on "ion" and "plasmajet" rockets, which produce thrust by electrical means and which, incidentally, can only be used for driving spaceships, not airplanes.)

A not very efficient atomic propulsion system, such as might reasonably be developed round the turn of this century, would enable us to attain speeds in the 1,000,000 m.p.h. category. This would mean Mars in less than two days—and Venus in one (though starting and stopping would extend these times somewhat)!

A million miles an hour is such a nice round figure that one is tempted to see what impression it would make on interstellar distances—since it certainly deflates interplanetary ones. The result is startling; even the very nearest of the stars would be almost three thousand years away.

We want a few more zeroes on our speedometer. What about 10,000,000 m.p.h.? Well, there's no theoretical reason why it should be impossible in the frictionless vacuum of space. The atom contains enough energy, if we are smart enough to apply it in the right way. And when a thing is possible in theory, it's always done in practice sooner or later. So—Proxima Centauri in only three hundred years.

One hundred million m.p.h.? Yes, even that's still not asking too much of atomic energy. However, we'll need to learn a few new tricks, such as the *total* conversion of matter into energy, not the annihilation of the miserable fraction of a per cent which is all that our present atomic devices achieve. That would take us to the nearest star in thirty years; still too long, but the figures are beginning to look reasonable at last. One more jump and we're nearly there.

One billion m.p.h.? I'm sorry—no. A new factor has come into the picture. On our way to that extra zero, we've passed the speed limit of the Universe. It happens to be 670,000,000 m.p.h. and is a limit that's rigorously enforced. It is the velocity of light—more usually quoted as 186,000 miles a second.

If the theory of relativity is correct—and all the evidence of the past fifty years indicates that it is—nothing can ever surpass this speed, and it would require an infinite amount of energy merely to reach it. Why this should be so is a complicated story which I have no intention of going into here; all that matters at the moment is that the velocity of light is not just an arbitrary figure, but is bound up with the very structure of the Universe. Even if you could, in theory, exceed it, you wouldn't be in our space and time any longer; you'd be somewhere else—if there *is* somewhere else.

The velocity of light, therefore, appears to set a limit to the speed with which any object can move through space. That speed may be approached more and more closely as propulsion systems improve, but it can never be reached, still less exceeded. If this is the case, time or travel between even the closest star systems can never be less than four or five years; between *inhabited* star systems, in our fairly crowded corner of the Galaxy, we might not be far out if we fix the lower limit of travel time as ten years.

This is a good deal longer than we would like, especially as the return trip still has to be considered. But can anyone seriously argue that it is an absolutely insuperable objection to interstellar flight? Of course not; as soon as the propulsion problems were solved, there would be members even of our ephemeral species who would be prepared to devote a quarter of their lives to the supreme adventure by contacting new races, new civilizations on the other side of the stellar abyss.

Recent progress in medical science may be of assistance here. Suspended animation—the deliberate production of a trancelike state in which the subject is unaware of the progress of time—is no longer a fantasy. It can be induced for short periods by drugs or cold, and it does not require much imagination to suppose that what the dormouse can do men may also be able to achieve. The distances between the stars will no longer seem so terrifying if we can sleep our way across them.

In any event, there is no need to assume that exploring vessels designed to cross interstellar space would carry living crews; it is much more likely that the first ones would not. All the rockets we have so far launched beyond the atmosphere carried recording instruments; spaceships which set out on journeys of indefinite duration and uncertain goal would be purely automatic, controlled by elaborate electronic brains which had been conditioned to perform one task—to gather all the information they could, and to bring it safely home. Since we will be able to build such robot scouts ourselves in the near future, other races must have had them for ages, and sooner or later they will come sniffing round our Earth.

Sooner or later. That, perhaps, is the crux of the whole matter. Visitors from space may have landed on our planet dozens—hundreds—of times during the long, empty ages while Man was still a dream of the distant future. Indeed, they could have landed on 90 per cent of the Earth as recently as two or three hundred years ago—and we would never have heard of it. If one searches through old newspapers and local records, one can find large numbers of curious incidents that could be interpreted as visitations from space. That stimulating if eccentric writer Charles Fort made a collection of such occurrences in his book *Lo!* and one is inclined to give them more weight than any comparable modern reports, for the simple reason that they happened long before anyone had ever thought of space travel. Yet at the same time one cannot take them *too* seriously, because before scientific education was widespread even the commonest celestial phenomena—meteors, comets, auroras and so on—gave rise to the most incredible stories. As they still do, in fact.

Going further back in time, it has been suggested that some of the legends and myths of prehistory, perhaps even the weird entities of many pagan religions, may have been inspired by glimpses of beings from other worlds. But this is pure and unprofitable speculation—unprofitable for the reason that it can never be proved or disproved, but only argued endlessly.

Do we have to wait ten years or a thousand years before the next ship calls? Or if none has ever called before, when will our Earth's billions of years of isolation be ended? It may be that our first meeting with alien intelligences is already far nearer to us in time than Columbus' landing in the New World.

One would like to think that we will be the discoverers, not the discovered. Yet perhaps when we leave the snug little confines of the Solar System, we may meet a bored reception committee which greets us with the words: "Taken your time, haven't you? Welcome to the Galactic Federation; here's the book of rules."

Or—and this is the most depressing thought of all— perhaps we have already been blacklisted. It provides a very simple, and horribly plausible, explanation for our apparent lack of visitors to date.

The neighbors may already know everything about us; who can blame them, therefore, if they've kept a few light-years away?

★ THE SUN

★

★ IF Dr. Gallup were to ask a fair sample of the public the straightforward question: "What is the nearest star?" the replies would probably run something like this:

> 95%—"How's that again?"
> 3%—"Alpha Centauri"
> 2%—"Proxima Centauri"

They would all be wrong, even the erudite 2 per cent who knew that Proxima was a fraction of a light-year closer to Earth than its companion, Alpha. For the nearest star is— the Sun.

It took the human race quite a few thousand years to discover this fact, for no two classes of object could be more unlike than the dazzling, burning Sun and the coldly scintillating stars. But remove the Sun to a million times its present distance, and it would become an undistinguished though still easily visible star. It is merely the Sun's extreme closeness—a trifling 93,000,000 miles—that gives it such overwhelming importance in terrestrial affairs.

The true nature of the Sun was a complete mystery until very recent times, and indeed it was only about twenty years ago that astronomers began to have some idea of what makes it function. Today, thanks to the patient detective work of generations of scientists, we have not only learned the secret of the Sun, but in the achievement of nuclear fusion we have ignited its fires here on Earth, with awesome consequences for the future of mankind.

To the ancients, the possibility of ever learning anything definite about the Sun must have seemed not only vain, but presumptuous. However, it is most unwise to set limits to knowledge and discovery, as is proved by the sad example of the eighteenth-century philosopher who remarked: "If one thing is certain, it is that we shall never know what the stars are made of." But today, thanks to the spectroscope, we have more accurate knowledge of the composition of stars trillions of miles away than we have of the earth beneath our feet.

All atoms, when they are sufficiently heated, become tiny transmitting stations—but they broadcast light, not radio waves. What is more, the wave length of that light is as characteristic of the particular atom involved as is a fingerprint of an individual man. The spectroscope can take the light of the Sun and spread it out into a colored band yards in length—a band crossed with thousands of lines which betrays the Sun's compostion as clearly as if the astronomer could grab a sample of it for chemical analysis. All the ordinary elements are present in the Sun, but two of them— hydrogen and helium—are vastly more abundant than all the others put together. The composition of the Sun, therefore, is quite different from that of the Earth, which is mostly made of oxygen and silicon. This was rather a blow to the theory that the Earth was once part of the Sun, but it has been able to survive thanks to some skillful footwork.

As soon as fairly accurate measurements of the Sun's distance and size (diameter 864,000 miles—or a hundred times that of the Earth) became available about three centuries ago, astronomers had a major problem on their hands, though just how major it was they didn't realize for another century. The amount of energy which the Earth receives from the Sun is enormous; it is roughly equivalent to a one-kilowatt electric heater on *every square yard* of our planet's surface. But the earth itself intercepts only a minute fraction of the Sun's rays; most of the energy goes rushing past into space and is, from our admittedly rather self-centered point of view, completely wasted. The total waste, if you like nice round figures, is approximately half a million, million million, million horsepower.

Where does all that energy come from? Even more important, how long is it going to last?

In the Victorian era, scientists began to ask these questions more and more insistently, and a splendid fight developed between the astronomers and the geologists. The problem was this—no source of energy known to science could possibly keep the Sun as a going concern for the periods of time that the geologists demanded. If the Sun was made of the best-quality coal, for example, it would have burned itself out in a couple of thousand years. It was obvious, therefore, that chemical energy was quite insufficient to power the Sun.

The astronomers racked their brains to think of an alternative, and at last they thought they had found one. The Sun, they decided, obtained its energy from its slow contraction under gravity. But if the Sun was contracting, it must once have been bigger, and it was not hard to calculate how long ago it had been since it had engulfed the Earth. The answer came to approximately fifty million years—which obviously set an upper limit to the age of the Earth.

At the beginning of the Victorian age, fifty million years seemed long enough to satisfy everyone, even those infidels who did not agree with Archbishop Ussher that the world was created in 4004 B.C. Then the evidence of geology began to accumulate, and it was soon obvious that fifty, a hundred —even five hundred—million years was simply not long enough to have allowed for all the changes which our planet has seen. The geologists pointed to the mountains that had been worn away, the chalk beds miles thick that had been laid down on the beds of vanished seas—and told the astronomers to go and look for a few more zeros. The argument was quite acrimonious, but the geologists always won because fossils are heavier than slide rules.

Not until the discovery of radioactivity was the paradox resolved, as the astronomers realized that there were gigantic stores of energy locked up in the atoms themselves. There could be no doubt that the Sun was able to tap that energy, which was sufficient to keep it shining steadily for thousands of millions of years. That took care of the past—and of the future too, as far ahead as anyone cared to look.

For several decades there was much speculation about the precise means by which the Sun released the energy of matter. Some elements—radium, for example—are naturally unstable and continuously give out energy, until they have decayed into less spendthrift substances, such as lead. But even if the Sun were made of radium—a highly unlikely assumption—that could not account for so vast a generation of power over so long a period of time. The Sun must have learned the secret of releasing energy from "ordinary" matter.

In the history of the world, there has been no more momentous quest than the search for that secret—uncannily foreshadowed in the legend of Prometheus, who brought fire from heaven to earth at the price of having his own body continually devoured. The first major clue came as long ago as 1868, when the spectroscope revealed in the Sun the lines of an element not yet discovered on Earth. The new element was given the appropriate name of "helium," and, after an intensive search, was found to be present in our atmosphere in minute quantities.

Helium, though it aroused a great deal of interest because of the unusual way in which it was found, seemed no more than a scientific novelty, and nothing could have appeared of less practical importance. But it was a major milestone on the road which was to lead, eighty-four years later, to the hundred-mile-long cloud above Eniwetok Atoll, and, beyond that, to the promise of eternal power for all the machines that Man would ever build.

We now know that helium is the ash which is left when hydrogen is burnt in the atomic furnace of the Sun. But the type of "burning" that takes place in the Sun is as much fiercer than ordinary combustion as the flame of a blowtorch is warmer than the pale glow of a firefly. It is an atomic, not a chemical process, and takes place at temperatures of millions instead of thousands of degrees. The Sun's interior, in fact, is far too hot for fire, as we know it, to exist.

The solar transmutation of hydrogen to helium, with its accompanying enormous release of energy, is a complex process involving several intermediate stages, and is quite different in detail from the reactions which take place in the H-bomb—though the final result is the same. The Sun also operates on a slightly larger scale; every second of time, some four million tons of matter are converted into raw energy. As the Department of Defense has unaccountably failed to answer my courteous letter asking for precise details of the H-bomb's composition, the following figure is only approximate, but will not be more than a zero astray in either direction. We would have to explode ten billion H-bombs *every second* if we wanted to equal the energy output of the Sun.

Deep down in the solar core, under the influence of pressures and temperatures beyond all imagination, the atoms of hydrogen are fused together to form helium, and the released energy batters its way up to the surface of the Sun, hundreds of thousands of miles above. Then, in the form of light, heat and other radiations, it spreads out into space to be lost in the uttermost limits of the Universe—apart from the tiny fraction which is intercepted by the Earth and the other planets, and which makes life possible on at least one of them.

No man has even seen the Sun, or ever will. Only a small part of its radiation—the narrow band of visible light—leaks down through our atmosphere, which acts as a filter eliminating most of the ultraviolet and X rays which without its protection would continually bombard us. When men leave the atmosphere and enter the direct solar rays, they will have to be shielded by the walls and windows of their spaceships. An unprotected man out in space—even assuming that he could still breathe—would die in a few minutes from acute sunburn.

Much of the effort now going into the building of satellite rockets is concerned with attempts to measure the Sun's radiations before they enter the atmosphere, so that we can get a true picture of what the Sun "looks like" when *all* its rays are taken into account. This work will have two immediate practical consequences, as well as endless indirect ones. The solar rays absorbed in the upper atmosphere have a great, though still unknown, effect on the weather, and also on short-wave radio communication. There are times when the Sun sends out sudden spurts of ultraviolet light that cause such intense electrification of the upper air that all long-distance radio circuits are disrupted.

In the last few years it has also been discovered that the Sun itself is a powerful though erratic radio transmitter. The outer layers of the Sun—its atmosphere, if one can use that term in connection with a body which is entirely gaseous—are convulsed by great storms which are often many times as large as our world, and which are visible in telescopes as black areas on the Sun's shining surface. Occasionally these areas, known as sunspots, are large enough to be seen by the naked eye, and for some reason which is still unknown they act as intense generators of radio waves. So also, on a smaller scale, does the Sun's beautiful and mysterious envelope, the corona, which can be seen in its full glory only during the magic moments of a total eclipse.

If we could "see" the Sun by its radio waves instead of its light waves we would not recognize it as the same object. It would appear much larger, and not even circular in shape. Normally it would be an irregular oval, slowly changing its shape from week to week. The brilliance of its surface would be very uneven; to the radio eye, the sunspots and corona would be the brightest portions, and the rest would be relatively dark. At rare intervals, for a few minutes at a time, a tiny portion of the disk would erupt in a blaze of radio brilliance so fierce that the Sun might shine for a little while with hundreds of times its normal intensity. This outburst would be a "flare," one of the most spectacular and least understood items in the Sun's extensive repertory of curious phenomena.

In recent years it has been possible to make motion-picture films of events on the surface of the Sun, and by speeding them up several hundred times to project on the screen the entire life story of cataclysmic solar events which may occupy hours of times and quadrillions—not millions—of cubic miles of space. Some of these films are awe-inspiring: they show immense fountains of flame spurting to heights of a hundred thousand miles from the Sun's edge; bridges of fire which could span a dozen earths forming and crumbling; exact replicas of A-bomb bursts—but a thousand times as large— shooting up into space.

But some of the occurrences that have been filmed on the Sun are not merely awe-inspiring; they are inexplicable, and when watching them one is acutely aware that one is seeing the action of forces completely beyond our understanding. Sometimes, for example, a slanting jet of incandescent gas will shoot out on a long, flat trajectory, reach its apex, *and then whip back along its original path*—just as if a shell at the peak of its flight decided to return to the sun. And sometimes, thousands of miles above the Sun's surface, cascades of glowing matter will start pouring down from no apparent source, as if they were created high in the solar atmosphere.

No one has yet been able to explain these events, which sometimes give the impression that time itself is running backward. Perhaps what we are seeing is not the actual movement of matter, but something analogous to electrical discharges—lightning flashes half a million miles in length.

In view of the fact that the Sun is purely gaseous, it is rather surprising that it has such a sharply defined surface, except in the areas disturbed by sunspots or sporadic eruptions. In the telescope, the edge of the Sun is such a geometrically perfect circle that it is much easier to imagine it composed of liquid than of gas. One reason for the "flatness" of the Sun's surface is its intense gravity, twenty-six times that of the Earth's. On the Sun, a 160-pound man would weigh almost two tons, but that would be the least of his worries.

Though there are many stars that wax and wane in brilliance, fortunately for us the Sun is not one of these so-called variables. Its output of heat and light has not changed by more than a few per cent during the course of human history, and perhaps not during the whole progress of geological time. (Though the suggestion has been made that solar changes were responsible for the Ice Ages, this theory is not very popular today.) The sunlight which warms us now has not altered its intensity since the first man walked the Earth.

Yet in the early days of Earth's history, even though the Sun was unchanged, the light that reached the surface of our planet was a fierce, searing flood of radiation that would have been fatal to all the life forms of our age. The atmospheric filters which protect us now had not then formed, and the raw sunlight that today exists only in space a hundred miles up could pour down almost unhindered upon the seas and continents of the ancient Earth.

And what of the future? Despite its size and the inconceivable stores of hydrogen still untapped within it, the Sun cannot maintain its present output forever, though it is still good for many billion years. In the present state of world affairs, what will happen when the Sun starts to run out of fuel around the year A.D. 10,000,000,000, give or take a few billion, seems something which no sensible person would worry about. So we will do just that.

The obvious assumption is that the Sun will gradually cool down to a dull red and finally gutter out into extinction; the wonderful closing chapter of H. G. Wells' masterpiece, *The Time Machine,* gives a description of the dying Sun based on this hypothesis. But as is so often the case in science, the obvious assumption is not the correct one. The Sun is not cooling down; it is warming up.

The effect on the weather will not be noticeable for about ten thousand million years, but then things will start to happen in a hurry. As the Sun uses up its hydrogen fuel and the helium "ash" begins to accumulate around its core, the solar furnace will burn hotter and hotter. It may seem strange that the Sun should do this as it runs out of fuel; the reason is that the thickening blanket of helium will bank up the central fires, and so increase the rate of burning, if we may continue to use our analogy from ordinary combustion. So, like a gambler who squanders his resources more and more frantically as he comes to their end, the Sun will go out in a final blaze of glory. Within a span of a mere five million years it will increase its brilliance a hundredfold, melting down the Earth and the inner planets into balls of glowing lava. Then it will collapse swiftly to a tiny star only a few thousand miles in diameter, becoming one of the fantastically dense "white dwarfs" in which the mass of an entire sun is packed into the volume of a planet.

It will still be very bright, but from the orbit of the Earth it will be so small that it will show no visible disk and will appear to give little more heat than the full Moon does today. The minute star which finally gutters to extinction amid the corpses of the planets will not be anything which we of today would recognize as the Sun.

So, at least, runs the current theory of solar evolution, but to claim that this is an accurate description of what *must* happen to the Sun would be very rash indeed. We are learning all the time, and with new knowledge our picture of the Sun is continually becoming more complicated. And even when we have attained a complete understanding of the processes taking place inside the Sun, we cannot be sure that external factors—clouds of interstellar dust into which it may run, for example—may not write new and unexpected chapters in its history.

A lot may happen to the Sun, and to the Earth, in the millions of centuries that lie ahead. Certainly we need have no fear of the Sun misbehaving in the next few thousand years. And after that, it won't matter. If it gets uncomfortable here on Earth, we'll go somewhere else.

★　WHAT CAN WE DO ABOUT THE WEATHER?
★

★ THERE is no man who has not cursed the weather at some time in his life. He may be a holidaymaker, watching the storm clouds cover the Sun; a farmer, fighting to save his parched crops—or an emperor, listening to the blizzard that is burying his armies and his dreams beneath a blanket of white. Each will have felt, in varying degree, the same helpless frustration; each will have wondered if someday, somehow, the apparently arbitrary pattern of rain and sun might be influenced by human needs and wishes.

Until a decade ago, this seemed as futile a hope as any in the extensive category of Man's aspirations. Today, it is no longer completely vain. There is still not a great deal that we can do about the weather—but it is at least beginning to take *some* notice of our activities.

The component of weather which is of the most direct importance to mankind is, of course, rainfall. Without the continual circulation of fresh water from sea to cloud to land and back to sea, most of the world would be a barren desert. Though there are many fortunate regions which have ample rain for their needs, vast arid zones exist which would be fertile if only rain could be induced to fall upon them.

Many primitive, and some not-so-primitive, peoples have tried their hands at attracting rain. The Zuñi Indians of New Mexico, for example, were famous for their rain dances. These usually began at the summer solstice, when the rays of the rising Sun struck the same place five mornings in succession. At the beginning of the ceremony, a boy impersonating the fire god would light a cedar branch and set fire to dry grass, on the theory that the smoke clouds would attract rain clouds. So, by applying the principles of sympathetic magic, the Indians arrived at much the same position as our modern rainmakers, who try to seed clouds with their silver-iodide smoke generators. It would be quite a difficult feat to explain to a Zuñi medicine man why *our* technique is scientific and his was merely superstition.

The Zuñi dancers, painted with yellow mud and carrying live tortoises, who probably did not enjoy the proceedings, would dance all night and then the rest of the next day, watching the sky for the first clouds to arrive. If no rain fell, they would know that they'd done something wrong and would try again, continuing their dances as long as necessary. That is one beauty of rainmaking; it always works *eventually*, though sometimes you may have to wait a few weeks or months for the pay-off.

It is hard for most of us, who take ample supplies of water for granted, to realize what rain means to people living in arid lands. It dominates their thoughts, their religion, their art. One of the Zuñi songs, chanted while the men danced and the women ground corn, symbolizes this preoccupation in these naïve yet moving words:

Lovely! See the cloud, the cloud appear!
Lovely! See the rain, the rain draw near!

> Who spoke?
> 'Twas the little corn-ear
> High on the tip of the stalk
> Saying while it looked at me
> Talking aloft there—
> Ah, perchance the floods
> Hither moving,
> Ah, may the floods come this way!

Curiously enough, other tribes who lived in well-watered regions such as Mississippi, and therefore had no need to evoke rain, evolved dances to drive storms away. To them, storms were symbols of war, and bad weather was a disaster if a peace ceremony was in progress. After heeding a Zuñi chant like the one above, a timid and uncertain rain cloud might well be badly confused by such an incantation as this:

> Away, away dark clouds, away!
> Leave the sky!
> Go far away, dark clouds, today,
> Leave the sky!

Yet perhaps with New Mexico pulling, and Mississippi pushing, something ought to happen in the general area of Texas.

More sophisticated peoples, feeling that Nature might not respond to invocations, have tried direct action by shooting cannon or rockets into rain clouds. The argument seems to have been that a shock or concussion might cause a cloud to drop its burden of water, and this idea is not completely absurd. A shock wave produces compression and, after it has passed, expansion of the air; this expansion, in turn, causes local cooling, which in theory could produce condensation in moisture-laden air. Today, everyone has seen this effect with his own eyes; the vapor trail behind a high-flying jet is caused in precisely this manner. And in some of the Pacific A-bomb tests, intense local rainfall was produced around the point of explosion; in movies that have been released, clouds can be seen forming like magic along the expanding front of the shock wave.

However, it is most unlikely that gunfire has ever produced any appreciable rainfall, for an explosion at ground level would have spent all its force by the time it reached an altitude where it might conceivably have some effect. After the First World War there was a widespread popular belief —reminiscent of the recent H-bomb debate—that the Flanders bombardment had produced abnorally bad weather. We can now look back with supercilious amusement upon such presumption, for today we have the doubtful privilege of being able to release, *in a single explosion,* more energy than was liberated by all the guns and shells and bombs of World War I.

During the Second World War, the Royal Air Force made a rather determined effort to Do Something About the Weather, if only on a local basis. All too often, a bomber squadron would take off to Germany only to discover, when it had completed its mission and returned to England, that its base had been closed down by fog. Many planes and crews were lost for this reason, and the "boffins"—as the R.A.F. affectionately christened its civilian scientists—were called upon to produce an answer.

That answer was FIDO (Fog, Intense, Dispersal Of), one of the war's most spectacular yet least publicized secret weapons. I was fortunate enough to be associated with the tests of the biggest FIDO installation ever built, on a large airfield in Cornwall, not far from Land's End. The runway was lined on either side with a double row of pipes—four or five miles of them in all—which conveyed gasoline to long rows of burners. When they were in action, they consumed fuel at the awesome rate of 100,000 gallons an hour (I trust that this figure is no longer a well-kept secret from the British taxpayer) and formed multiple walls of flame the full length of the runway.

At night, with the fog rolling in from the Atlantic, a FIDO operation was like a scene from Dante's *Inferno.* The roar of the flames filled the air and made speech difficult; they created such an updraft that small stones on the edge of the runway were picked up and tossed around by the air currents. As far as the eye could see, the yellow walls of fire, taller than a man, stretched away into the foggy night. The miles of burners were pumping heat into the air at the rate of 10,000,000 horsepower, cutting a long, narrow trench through the fog, down which the returning bombers could find their way to the ground.

I have known nights when the fog was so thick that visibility was less than ten feet—but standing in the middle of the runway, with the flames roaring on either side, one could see the stars shining overhead. FIDO worked by brute force, and the development of radar made it obsolete; but it did show what could be done if the incentive was sufficiently great—and expense was no object.

It was not until 1946 that, for the first time, a method of affecting weather without the use of enormous amounts of energy appeared on the scene, and rainmaking changed from a superstition into a science. In that year Vincent Schaefer, at the General Electric Laboratories, discovered that "dry ice"—solid carbon dioxide—could cause the precipitation of myriads of minute ice crystals in water-laden, supercooled air. Further experiments showed conclusively that *in the right circumstances* solid carbon dioxide was so effective a "seeding" agent that a few pounds of it could trigger off the precipitation of millions of times its own weight of rain.

The process works because the water vapor in the atmosphere does not normally condense directly into rain, but first forms ice crystals which melt before they reach the ground. In turn each crystal of ice must have a dust particle, or something equivalent, to act as its foundation—very much as a pearl grows around an almost invisible speck of irritant in an oyster. If the atmosphere is sufficiently cold, and contains enough water vapor, then the particles of solid CO_2 can start the chain reaction which may make a cloud release its precious burden.

"Dry ice" has now been largely superseded by silver iodide, the crystals of which are very similar in shape to the basic hexagonal unit from which all snowflakes are built up. When a smoke of invisibly small silver-iodode crystals is released into a cloud, ice forms rapidly around them and snow starts to fall. A small spoonful of silver iodide, costing a couple of cents, can produce 10,000,000,000,000,000 snowflakes *under favorable conditions*.

That last phrase is the key to all rainmaking experiments. No cloud seeding, or any other technique, can produce rain out of a dry atmosphere—or even out of a wet one, if the temperature in the cloud is too high to permit condensation.

There is still a great deal of argument among meteorologists about the effectiveness of rain making, and some early optimistic promises have been rather drastically scaled down.

But there seems little doubt that scientific cloud seeding can increase the rainfall by 10 or 15 per cent—and there are circumstances where such percentages are very much worth while. Such cities as Dallas, Fort Worth and Oklahoma City have recently signed rainmaking contracts which appear to have netted them several million dollars worth of extra water.

There is also some evidence that the number of destructive tornadoes has decreased in areas where cloud seeding has taken place. Possibly, continued "milking" of rain clouds prevents the build-up of unstable conditions which could lead to tornadoes, and if this fact can be definitely established it will be an important step forward in weather control. However, it is extremely difficult to prove anything in this elusive field, where so many variables are involved. Skeptical meteorologists can always argue that any behavior of the weather, however freakish, is due entirely to natural causes. Only by the accumulating of statistics over long periods of time is it possible to detect the results of human intervention.

Before we can hope to achieve anything more impressive than the premature puncturing of overladen clouds, we will need not only more power but also more knowledge. As far as the latter is concerned, we are rapidly accumulating it, and there is no doubt that artificial satellites will make possible an enormous advance in meteorology. For the first time we are able to study our Earth from outside, and can measure the radiations falling upon it from space—radiations hidden from our view until now by the thick screen of the atmosphere itself.

"Weather," is, in fact, no more than the local behavior of the atmosphere, as it perpetually adjusts to influences both cosmic and terrestrial. The human race lives inside a steam engine eight thousand miles across, operated by sun power, and with oceans for boilers and mountain ranges for condensers. The entire machine rotates on its axis every twenty-four hours, and its parts are most irregularly shaped—so it is hardly surprising that we have not yet been able to figure accurately what will happen next at any given spot.

The total energy involved in the circulation of the atmosphere is enormous; to keep all the winds of the world on the move would require the energy of a million atom bombs a *day*. We can hardly expect, therefore, that a single atom bomb would have an appreciable effect on the general weather picture; one might as well imagine that, if the entire population of Washington or Cleveland were shouting at once, the voice of one extra man would be noticed.

Yet one man's voice can start an avalanche thundering down a mountainside, its infinitesimal energy triggering the fall of millions of tons of snow. It is, therefore, by no means impossible that a strategically detonated bomb could produce large-scale alterations, just as the few grams of silver iodide dropped upon a cloud can initiate a downpour. Unfortunately, we know far too little about the causes of weather to calculate exactly where to apply the "push" which may lead—perhaps days later and half the globe away—to some desired result. The consequences of error here could so serious that one hopes that no attempt is made to alter the weather on a large scale until we know enough to be able to make forecasts with complete accuracy.

The widespread popular belief that A- and H-bomb tests have been responsible for recent abnormal weather is not supported by the facts. The National Academy of Science now has a "Committee on Meteorological Aspects of Atomic Radiation," which after studying the available evidence has come to the conclusion of that there has been nothing unusual about the weather of the last few years.

One need not go back very far into the Pre-Atomic Age to match everything in the way of droughts or floods, hurricanes or tornadoes, that the current decade has produced.

Strangely enough, it is a much homelier and less terrifying of Man's activities which may have already produced a noticeable effect upon the weather—indeed, upon the climate itself. For the last fifty years, the globe has been warming up. It is true that the average temperature rise is only about two degrees, but that has been enough to start the glaciers receding in many parts of the world.

A rise of one degree per generation is a fantastic rate of increase; Nature seldom moves as swiftly as this. We may have been helping her. To a very large extent, the temperature of the Earth is determined by the amount of solar heat which the atmosphere can retain. The air above us acts like the glass in a greenhouse, trapping many of the heat waves which would otherwise bounce right back into space.

And the constituent of the air which is most responsible for this "greenhouse effect" is carbon dioxide, the gas produced by all our countless fires, furnaces and internal combustion engines.

Every year we put not millions but billions of tons of CO_2 into the air. Most of it is promptly taken out again by growing plants as they mix it with water, sunlight and chlorophyll to produce starch and oxygen. Yet there may be a net gain, and that gain may have been sufficient to explain the upward temperature trend of the last half century.

The end of the short-lived age of fossil fuels is already in sight; soon—in one or two centuries at the most—we will have squandered the world's resources of oil and coal, accumulated over so many geological aeons. This no longer means disaster, for atomic energy has arrived in time to save our civilization from perishing through lack of power. We are moving into a brighter and cleaner age, as the smoke of a myriad fires and blast furnaces and automobiles ceases to stain the skies. But for that very reason, it may also be a colder age.

This suggests that, paradoxically enough, it may be easier to affect climate—the long-range pattern of temperature and moisture—than to control the behavior of the weather, which is a local, short-term phenomenon, possibly subject to random and therefore unpredictable influences. The climate of Earth is determined to no small extent by the immense quantities of ice locked up at the poles, and that ice remains perpetually frozen, despite the twenty-four-hour-long summer days, because the Sun's heat is reflected off the blinding white wastes and has no chance of being absorbed. If that ice could once be removed, it would never re-form on the same scale. The darker, exposed soil would collect and keep so much of the Sun's warmth now lost to us that the Earth would balance off its incoming and outgoing radiation at a higher temperature level.

If such a melting of the polar ice could be achieved, we would gain a fifth continent; the Antarctic, with its unknown wealth of minerals, might be the home of new nations and new civilizations.

In a few decades, as fission gives way to fusion and hydrogen energy replaces the costly and poisonous power of uranium, we may be able to thaw out the ancient ice that sheets the poles. But there may be a better way; why not let the Sun itself do the work?

On a bright winter's day, spread a sheet of any black material across a snowdrift—and watch how quickly it sinks as it melts its way downward. The trapped sunlight is burning a way into the snow, now that it is absorbed and no longer reflected back into the sky. Even at the South Pole, the radiation received from the Sun at Midsummer's Day equals the heat from a network of one-kilowatt electric fires, spaced five feet apart.

Catch that energy for a few years, perhaps by dusting the snows with carbon black in some form that would not be easily dispersed, and we might be able to make a permanent impression upon our planet's polar caps. However, the price of Antarctica might be higher than we would care to pay, for the sea level over the whole Earth would rise at least a hundred feet.

The pros and cons of such a scheme would, therefore, have to be very carefully weighed—though there is something rather attractive about the idea of New York as a semitropical Venice, with gondola-buses letting off the passengers at the tenth floor. . . .

It will be a long time before we attempt to interfere with the climate of our planet on such a scale as this; we are more likely to content ourselves, for a few centuries to come, with air-conditioning on an ever-increasing scale. The first air-conditioned business and shopping centers, covering several blocks, are now being planned; soon entire cities will follow suit. After all, if we can control our living conditions inside our homes and offices, and can predict what will happen outside with sufficient accuracy to make our vacation arrangements, what more do we *really* need?

Well, one day we will need a great deal more. We lie between two Ice Ages, and we do not know when the next one is due. Sooner or later, the glaciers will start to move once more, grinding down from the poles to reconquer the land they relinquished little more than fifteen thousand years ago.

Our ancestors met that challenge in the only way they could. They retreated; but we will stand and fight.

★ OH FOR THE WINGS . . .
★

★ THE rapid development of automation now makes it virtually certain that there can be no escape from an age of compulsory leisure in the not-too-distant future. It is also equally certain that most of mankind won't be content to occupy its spare time exclusively with painting, ballet dancing, orchestral composition, poetry recital, monumental sculpting and similar aesthetic activities. Which leads us to conclude that one of the greatest benefactors of the human race in the years ahead will be the man who can invent a new sport.

A completely new and original sport is a very rare invention indeed. We are lucky enough to have witnessed the birth of a major one—skin diving—during the last decade. It now seems quite possible that an even more spectacular and unexpected recreation will arrive in the quite near future. That new sport may be—flying.

Before you ask indignantly where I've been hiding since 1903, let me make clear exactly what I mean. The flying I refer to is one of man's most ancient dreams, forgotten since the internal-combustion engine gave us (at a price) the freedom of the air. It is flight *by muscle power alone*—the practical achievement of the legend of Daedalus, the conversion into the reality of Leonardo da Vinci's sketches.

We are so accustomed to the roar of thousands and tens of thousands of horsepower in the sky that we have taken it for granted that muscle-powered flight is an aerodynamic impossibility as far as human beings are concerned. Our bodies, it has been generally assumed, are far too heavy and underpowered for the job. And anyway—who cares?

Let's deal with the last point first. A great many people *would* care, if they had the slightest idea that such a feat as man-powered flight was even theoretically possible. There is always a sense of achievement in doing something without mechanical aid, and discovering the limits of the human body's ability. Only the most torpid and unimaginative of men can fail to feel some sense of excitement at the idea of competing with the birds in their own element, on their own terms.

The development of aerodynamics as an exact science now allows us to analyze the problem of manned flight as a straight-forward engineering proposition. There is a certain whimsical interest in the fact that the subject is now being studied by a group of young British aerodynamicists at the College of Aerodynamics, Cranfield—in the intervals between calculating what happens to vehicles re-entering the Earth's atmosphere from outer space at twenty times the speed of sound.

The crux of the problem is how much power a man can develop. For very short periods (say a couple of seconds) this may be as much as $1\frac{1}{2}$ h. p., if legs and arms are used simultaneously. This is equivalent to lifting one's own weight through five feet every second—a sort of high-jump performance, in fact. It obviously has no relevance to sustained, steady operating conditions, but may be of importance in connection with take-offs.

The *continuous* power which a man can produce for prolonged periods—up to an hour—is just under half a horsepower, and a little more if arms as well as legs are used. (.45 h.p. legs alone; .6 h.p. all limbs working.) When one looks at the disparity in size between a horse and a man, this figure is quite surprising. However, the definition of a horsepower—a rate of working of 550 feet pounds per second —was laid down at the beginning of the steam-engine age by James Watt, and we can be quite sure that he chose a small and skinny horse for his standard so that the performance of his engines would appear correspondingly impressive. Even then, he probably cooked the figures.

The basic problem of manned flight, therefore, is that of building an aircraft that can fly on a half-horsepower engine. This would be a considerable feat of aeronautical skill, and it is not certain that it is possible. What does appear to be possible, however, is to build a *two-man* machine that could be sustained in the air by muscle power alone. The point is that an aircraft carrying two men would have double the power, but much less than double the drag and weight, of a "single-engined" one, and would be correspondingly more efficient. It might be even better to have a still larger crew, all but one of its members pedaling furiously with hands and feet while the odd man out steered the machine and provided power with legs alone.

To concentrate on the minimum-sized, two-man machine, calculations made by B. S. Shenstone indicate that it would have to weigh about five hundred pounds (more than half that being the weight of the crew) and would have a wingspan of about sixty feet. The very large wingspan arises from the fact that the aircraft must have the extremely low wing loading—the amount of dead weight each square foot of wing area has to support—of about two pounds per square foot, as compared with the fifty or more pounds per square foot of a modern airliner (not to mention the hundred pounds per square foot and up of a supersonic fighter).

Incidentally, it might be mentioned that Mr. Shenstone is the Chief Engineer of British European Airways. His interest in this particular problem should cause no alarm to B.E.A. passengers; it is a purely private one and doesn't indicate that the company fears that its customers will ever have to get out and push.

The airframe would have to be extremely "clean," since no power could be wasted overcoming unnecessary drag, even at the low speed of 30 m.p.h., which is about the limit to be expected from such a vehicle. To obtain the required low drag, what is known as "boundary-layer control" would be needed. This involves sucking air from the wing through slots placed at strategic locations, thus preventing the build-up of turbulent eddies.

One of the most difficult engineering problems in the design would be getting the power out of the men and into the airscrew without too much loss through gears, chains or bearings. A very efficient transmission system would be required, as the crew would be at the front or center of the aircraft, and the propeller would probably be at the rear.

Without going into too many details which still remain for the experts on sub-subsonic flight to work out, we can get a fairly clear idea of the two-man aerial bicycle of the near future. It would look very much like one of today's gliders, and would be built from similar materials. The wing would be excessively long and thin—only about five feet wide at the roots, but with a total span of sixty feet. There would be no undercarriage, a spring-mounted skid serving for landing gear.

To keep frontal area to a minimum, the crew would sit— or even lie in a reclining position, like bobsled riders. The pilot would pedal with his feet and use his hands for control; the rear man would be working flat out with all his limbs.

There is one slight difficulty we haven't mentioned yet. Such an underpowered aircraft could fly, but it couldn't take off. It would have to be launched into the air like a glider by winch, catapult or rockets.

The take-off *could* be purely man-powered if the vehicle contained some energy-storing device which would be revved up by the crew while they were still on the ground, and then coupled to the propeller to give a brief burst of power. A spinning flywheel is the obvious example of such a device, but would be far too heavy to be practical. Perhaps a compressed-air system might do the trick, and would also solve the transmission problem. The crew could pedal away until they had built up starting pressure in a cylinder, and at the right moment this would be connected to a tiny piston engine driving the airscrew. The use of compressed-air lines instead of shafts or chains would simplify the engineering problems, but the increased weight and complexity of the system might make it impracticable.

In any event, it is clear that the aircycle will be a fairly expensive piece of machinery—at least as expensive as a glider, though of course the cost of production would fall sharply if the demand was sufficiently large. The two-man machines would certainly be within the reach of most sport clubs, colleges and athletic organizations. And as for the larger ones, it is obvious what their destiny would be.

It's about time that Harvard and Yale, not to mention Oxford and Cambridge, moved ahead with the times. Can't you picture the excitement as the beautifully streamlined aircraft, fragile and delicate as dragonflies, are brought out of their (ivy-covered) hangars? The crews—representing the highest weight-to-power ratio their colleges can muster—file into the long, slim fuselages and take their places in line astern. They won't see much of the race; but then they never did. Only the coxes under their tiny perspex blisters will know what is happening and will control the flight of the graceful, man-powered birds.

The propellers spin into invisibility, the rudders and ailerons swing back and forth as the controls are tested. The elastic launching cables have been attached; the two aircraft are lined up side by side, waiting for the starting signal.

They're off! Leaping from the ground under the smooth yet steady tug of the catapults, the two machines rise steeply into the sky. At the same instant the launching cables drop away; they're on their own now, as they head toward the starting line, at all of forty miles an hour, on the first lap of the unforgettable race of 19—.

What date shall we fill in there? As far as technical considerations are concerned, the aircraft could be ready in five or ten years at the most, and if anyone has a large fraction of a megabuck which they would like to donate to a spectacular but completely useless cause this time scale might be compressed.

Useless? That, it seems to me, is one of its chief virtues. A feeble and far-fetched case might be made out for some military applications, but only the dimmest of generals would be convinced by it—perhaps one who was still pining for the days of cavalry. Though the glider has been turned into a weapon of war, the man-powered airplane appears to have about as promising a military future as the crossbow.

Perhaps for this very reason we won't develop it. We may be so busy building rockets and starting on the conquest of space that we'll leave it to the twenty-first century to complete the conquest of the air.

Postscript

There have been further developments in this field since the above article was written. In England, the Royal Aeronautical Society has formed a Man Power Flight Group, and the Russians (here we go again!) have also set up a "Muscle Powered Flight Committee." The Aéro Club de France is organizing a competition for such aircraft, and the startling fact has emerged that it might have been won in 1936 by

Haessler and Villinger in Germany, who made several officially observed single-seat man-powered flights of over two hundred yards at heights of between three and fifteen feet.

Anyone who is interested in technical details will find a paper of great value by T. Nonweiler in the October, 1958, issue of the *Journal of the Royal Aeronautical Society*.

★ ACROSS THE SEA OF STARS
★

★ AT some time or other, and not necessarily in moments of depression or illness, most men have known that sudden spasm of unreality which makes them ask, "What am I doing here?" Poets and mystics all down the ages have been acutely aware of this feeling, and have often expressed the belief that we are strangers in a world which is not really ours.

This vague and disturbing premonition is perfectly accurate. We don't belong here, and we're on our way to somewhere else.

The journey began a billion years ago, when one of our forgotten ancestors crawled up out of the sea and so started life's invasion of the land. That great adventure was Nature's most spectacular triumph, but it was achieved at a heavy price in biological hardship—a price which every one of us continues to pay to this day.

We are so accustomed to our terrestrial existence that it is very hard for us to realize the problems that had to be overcome before life emerged from the sea. The shallow, sun-drenched water of the primitive oceans was an almost ideal environment for living creatures. It buffered them from extremes of temperature, and provided them with both food and oxygen. Above all, it sustained them, so that they were untouched by the crippling, crushing influence of gravity. With such advantages, it seems incredible that life ever invaded so hostile an environment as the land.

Hostile? Yes, though that is an adjective few people would apply to it. Certainly I would not have done so before I took up skin diving and discovered—as have so many

have done in eighty. What is really significant is richness and diversity of experience, and the use to which that is put by men and the societies they constitute. It is here that the conquest of space will produce an advance in complexity of stimulus even greater than that which occurred when life moved from water to land.

In the sea, every creature exists at the center of a little universe which is seldom more than a hundred feet in radius, and is usually much smaller. This is the limit set by underwater visibility, and though some information comes from greater distances by sound vibrations, the world of the fish is a very tiny place.

That of a land animal is thousands of times larger. It can see out to the horizon, miles away. And at night it can look up to the stars, those piercing points of light whose incredible explanation was discovered by Man himself more recently than the time of Shakespeare.

In space, there will be no horizon this side of infinity. There will be suns and planets without end, no two the same, many of them teeming with strange life forms and perhaps stranger civilizations. The sea which beats against the coasts of Earth, which seems so endless and so eternal, is as the drop of water on the slide of a microscope compared with the shoreless sea of space. And our pause here, between one ocean and the next, may be only a moment in the history of the Universe.

When one contemplates this awe-inspiring fact, one sees how glib, superficial and indeed downright childish are the conceptions of those science-fiction writers who merely transfer their cultures and societies to other planets. Whatever civilizations we may build on distant worlds will differ from ours more widely than mid-twentieth-century America differs from Renaissance Italy or, for that matter, from the Egypt of the Pharaohs. And the differences, as we have seen, will not merely be cultural; in the long run they will be organic as well. In a few thousand years of forced evolution, many of our descendants will be sundered from us by psychological and biological gulfs far greater than those between the Eskimo and the African pygmy.

The frozen wilderness of Greenland and the steaming forests of the Congo represent the two extremes of the climatic range that Man has been able to master without the use of advanced technology. There are much stranger environments among the stars, and one day we shall pit ourselves against them, employing the tools of future science to change atmospheres, temperatures and perhaps even orbits. Not many worlds can exist upon which an unprotected man could survive, but the men who challenge space will not be unprotected. They will remold other planets as we today bulldoze forests and divert rivers. Yet, in changing worlds, they will also change themselves.

What will be the thoughts of a man who lives on one of the inner moons of Saturn, where the Sun is a fierce but heatless point of light and the great golden orange of the giant planet dominates the sky, passing swiftly through its phases from new to full while it floats within the circle of its incomparable rings. It is hard for us to imagine his outlook on life, his hopes and fears—yet he may be nearer to us than we are to the men who signed the Declaration of Independence.

Go further afield to the worlds of other suns (yes, one day, we shall reach them, though that may not be for ages yet), and picture a planet where the word "night" is meaningless, for with the setting of one sun there rises another—and perhaps a third or fourth—of totally different hue. Try to visualize what must surely be the weirdest sky of all—that of a planet near the center of one of those close-packed star clusters that glow like distant swarms of fireflies in the fields of our telescopes. How strange to stand beneath a sky that is a solid shield of stars, so that there is no darkness between them through which one may look out into the Universe beyond. . . .

Such worlds exist, and one day men will live upon them. But why, it may reasonably be asked, should we worry about such remote and alien places when there is enough work to keep us busy here on Earth for centuries?

Let us face the facts; we do not have centuries ahead of us. We have aeons, barring accidents and the consequences of our own folly. A hundred million years will be but a small fraction of the future history of Earth. This is about the length of time that the dinosaurs reigned as masters of this planet. If we last a tenth as long as the great reptiles which we sometimes speak of disparagingly as one of Nature's fail-

ures, we will have time enough to make our mark on countless worlds and suns.

Yet one final question remains. If we have never felt
wholly at home here on Earth, which has mothered us for so
many ages, what hope is there that we shall find greater
happiness or satisfaction on the strange worlds of foreign
suns?

The answer lies in the dictinction between the race and the
individual. For a man "home" is the place of his birth and
childhood—whether that be Siberian steppe, coral island,
Alpine valley, Brooklyn tenement, Martian desert, lunar
crater, or mile-long interstellar ark. But for Man, home can
never be a single country, a single world, a single Solar
System, a single star cluster. While the race endures in
recognizably human form, it can have no one abiding place
short of the Universe itself.

This divine discontent is part of our destiny. It is one
more, and perhaps the greatest, of the gifts we inherited
from the sea that rolls so restlessly around the world.

It will be driving our descendants on toward a myriad of
unimaginable goals when the sea is stilled forever, and Earth
itself a fading legend lost among the stars.

★ OF MIND AND MATTER

★

★ For thousands of years the human race has debated, with singular lack of agreement, such questions as the
existence of the soul, the meaning of personality, the relationship between the mind and the body and—above all—the
possibility of survival after death. The fact that the debate
is still just as heated as when it began in the Late Neolithic
Period strongly suggests that the wrong questions have been
asked, and certain spectacular developments of the last
decade indicate, with equal force, that now is a good time
to recast them into a form that makes sense.

Those developments are purely scientific—a fact which
will upset a great many people with vested interests in some
of the pseudo-answers now current. They lie almost entirely

in the fields of biophysics, neurology and electronics, and at first sight it may seem improbable that such areas of modern technology could have any conceivable relation to the great questions of philosophy and religion.

But four centuries ago, it would have seemed equally unlikely that several thousand years of cosmological speculation, culminating in the poetic fantasies of *Paradise Lost*, could have been swept away in a few decades by a couple of lenses in a tube. Today, we are witnessing another scientific breakthrough, in an area that affects us much more personally than any astronomical discovery could possibly do.

It is now obvious that we are approaching, more closely than anyone would have dared to hope a few years ago, the basic secrets of life itself. Such fabulous tools as the electron microscope, which has given us clear pictures of the very building blocks of living organisms, are showing us how the bridge was crossed between the world of inorganic materials and the richer world of life. It is only a matter of time before that bridge is crossed again in some laboratory; whether that moment is ten or a hundred years from now is not in itself important. Many details of the fantastically complex electrochemistry of life will elude us for generations yet, but it cannot be doubted now that there is nothing inherently mysterious, or fundamentally unknowable, in the processes that build and power our bodies. That makes them none the less marvelous; real knowledge, when it dispels superstition, seldom diminishes awe. (For can the petty cosmos of Milton compare with the grandeur of the Universe we know today?)

It seems possible that the brain will hold its secrets longer than the body, but even here remarkable advances have been made toward an understanding of the processes of memory and reason—all the complex of phenomena which we group under the term "thought." In this case the scientific breakthrough has occurred at two distinct points: on the one hand the mechanism of the brain itself has been investigated, and on the other electronic devices have been built which show—often with startling realism—many of the behavior patterns of sentient creatures. And perhaps most significant of all, the large-scale development of giant computers has done much to destroy the illusion that there is something transcendental about the brain, beyond all possibility of duplication or imitation by machine.

Almost all the basic activities of the mind have now been reproduced, more or less successfully, by electronic means. Memory, purposeful reaction to the environment, ability to draw logical or mathematical conclusions—these are now commonplace features of machines being mass-produced for the commercial market. The ability to learn from past experience—to profit from mistakes so that they will not be made again—has also been demonstrated on the laboratory scale. Even the all-too-human attribute of total unpredictability can be incorporated in a machine if desired; and sometimes it *is* desirable, in carefully regulated amounts. (For there are problems that can drive both men and machines crazy if they try to solve them, and then the only thing to do is to make a random choice.)

The situation has been somewhat confused by the determination of the computer designers not to let the popular name "electronic brains" be applied to their offspring. For once, however, the public, and not the experts, is right. Today's computers *are* electronic brains by any reasonable definition of the phrase. It is true that they have the intelligence of single-minded tapeworms (though they usually possess much better memories), but this does not alter the basic situation.

Important though electronic computers will be (and indeed already are) in science, business and technology, it is their profound philosophical implications which we are concerned with here. For they have shown—in principle at least —that though Mind needs a vehicle, that vehicle can be of many forms.

Before we see where this leads us, it is necessary to deal with a persistent red herring. Many people have been so impressed by the gulf between even the most advanced electronic computer and the most moronic human mind that they have denied the possibility of bridging it. The brain of a man, it has been pointed out, contains approximately ten billion fundamental switching units, capable of cross-connection in an almost infinite number of ways. A much quoted "proof" that no electronic equivalent of the brain is possible states that such a machine would have to be as large as the Empire State Building and would need as much water as flows over Niagara to keep its billions of vacuum tubes cool.

It is amusing to see how quickly this has become an argument that such a machine is perfectly possible. Since the first computers were built, the bulky heat-generating vacuum tube has been largely replaced by the rice-grain-sized transistor. We no longer need the whole Empire State Building; one floor will do, and the existing plumbing will provide all the cooling water required. But even this reduction in scale has now been surpassed; the transistor itself is challenged by the yet tinier and still more efficient cryotron (a switch literally as big as a hair, operating on the principle of superconductivity). It is believed that one of today's giant computers could be packed into a small suitcase if it were redesigned with cryotrons as its fundamental circuit elements. So much, then, for the Empire State school of criticism.

All this does not mean that we will be able to build electronic equivalents of the human brain in the near or even remote future. But the feat is not intrinsically impossible, and when one looks back at the progress of technology during the past hundred years one would be very foolish indeed to declare categorically that this will never be achieved. Most top-rank computer scientists, if they let their hair down, would probably agree that sooner or later we will find ourselves dealing with mechanical entities which will pass every conceivable test for intelligence and self-awareness which we might apply to another human being. They will contain fewer units than many electronic systems already in existence—the telephone network of the United States, for example—though they will be a great deal more complicated.

A good many people find it somehow degrading to realize that the human brain, like the human body, is "only" an electro-chemical machine and flatly refuse to admit it. This attitude is completely absurd. The Taj Mahal is "only" a mass of stones; the roof of the Sistine Chapel only plaster and paint. *The material is unimportant; the pattern is all that matters*. Should an athlete feel that sport is worthless because of the undeniable fact that his body is an elaborate artifice of pumps, levers and elastic fibers? Of course not; indeed, it adds zest and interest to his performance. (It is no coincidence that the first man to run a mile in four minutes was a doctor.) It may well be that we will learn to think properly and effectively only when we know *how* we think.

We must not commit the elementary error of supposing

that the mechanism of the human brain is necessarily similar in detail to that of today's (or tomorrow's) electronic computers. It is certainly not so, if only because of the different structural elements involved. This, however, is quite unimportant; what matters is that memory, personality—all the components which make up every human being and distinguish him from all other men who have ever lived—are (   ) the by-product of data storage and processing in an extremely complex computer *of some kind*. (That blank parenthesis, by the way, is to allow you to insert the word "merely" if it helps your feelings. It will affect the situation just about as much as the actions of Kipling's "Village That Voted the Earth Was Flat.")

It may be no serious oversimplification to say that a man is the sum of his abilities (the circuit networks through which he observes the external world and decides what to do about it) and his memories (the storage banks holding his accumulated experience). There may be other components, but these are the basic ones which between them largely, and perhaps completely, account for the personality and behavior of every one of us.

The storage of information can be carried out in many ways—by marks on paper, by grooves in wax, by holes punched in cards—or, as Nature appears to do it, by coding based upon molecular structures like immensely elongated Yale keys. The physical basis is immaterial; as we have said before, only the pattern itself matters. And from this simple fact, the most awe-inspiring results follow. Even those readers who have found nothing surprising or controversial in what has gone before had better fasten their seat belts at this point.

One characteristic of a pattern is that it can be reproduced; a good example is the way in which endless indistinguishable copies of a symphony can be stamped out from a master recording. (Indistinguishable? Not strictly speaking, but the differences can be made so small that they are of no practical importance.) Now the duplication of a human personality would be an immensely more difficult problem—*but it is not a fundamentally different one*. We cannot at this primitive stage of our technology begin to guess how it could be achieved, any more than Beethoven could have imagined how a performance of the Ninth Symphony could be snatched out of time and saved for eternity.

The basic problem is that of recording and playing back —using those terms in a general sense—the vast quantity of information involved in defining personality and memory. Yet the actual storage space required is quite small. If Nature manages to compress the pattern of a human body into a couple of cells invisible to the eye, and the memories of a lifetime into a lump of jelly six inches across, is it expecting too much to suppose that Man may one day perform the same feat with a few cubic yards of electronics? After all, we could now pack the Library of Congress into a shoe box if we had to, and the amount of information there must be comparable with that defining an individual human being.

It therefore follows that, in a strictly scientific sense, reincarnation is theoretically possible. If one could reproduce the physical pattern of an individual down to the molecular fine-structure which is the library of the mind, there would be no way of distinguishing between the original and the duplicate. It would be totally meaningless to ask, "Which is *really* John Doe?" They would both be.

If you think that this is absurd fantasy, of no practical importance, you have a surprise coming. For it happened to *you* during the last few months; it will have happened to me by the time you read these words. This is a simple statement of fact—though a fact that could never have been imagined before the tools of modern science were turned upon the mechanism of life.

The atoms in our bodies are in a state of constant flux, being replaced so rapidly by others from the food we eat that we are completely rebuilt every few weeks. Even the bones are involved in this ceaseless ebb and flow of matter. Every one of us moves through the world like a flame, seeking fuel from his environment, assembling it into a momentary pattern, then rejecting the smoke and ash. Only the flame is—relatively—unchanging, until it gutters to extinction at the end of life.

It has been said that no man ever steps twice into the same river; it is almost equally true that no man ever looks at his face twice in the mirror. The flow of flesh may be slower than the movement of water to the sea, but it is no less inexorable.

We are involved, therefore, in a kind of continuous reincarnation almost as marvelous as any other type that has ever been postulated. At the same time, we can see that another popular idea of the mystics—transmigration through lower animals—can have no logical basis. The personality and memory of a human being could no more be squeezed into the limited storage capacity of any other vertebrate (still less invertebrate) than could the entire musical heritage of mankind be recorded on a six-inch disk.

The above argument now enables us to give a definite and somewhat unexpected answer to the ancient question of immortality. What happens to us when we die can differ in no significant way from what happens to the information punched on an I.B.M. card—when the card is burned. But suppose the information is also stored elsewhere (in what manner is immaterial) and is used to prepare a fresh card. There would then be no way of distinguishing between the old card and the new.

Some people may console themselves with the thought that such "master cards" (using the term in a completely general sense to mean any suitable storage device) may exist somehow, somewhere; others will consider such an attitude slightly egocentric. Yet even if no records are in existence from which anyone alive today could be recreated, this may not always be the case. If it seems absurd to talk of storing a human being on a few miles of tape, that is only because we cannot yet build the input and output devices which could perform the feat. If the day should ever come when this is possible, death will have lost its power over the minds of men.

I have little doubt that a great many people will consider these speculations naïvely mechanistic, because they cannot reconcile such imponderables as personality, intelligence— even the soul, if one cares to use the word—with the concepts of electronics or information theory. Such an attitude is a hangover from nineteenth-century materialism—though this charge will make many critics doubly indignant. By the word "machine," far too many otherwise educated people still envisage a contraption of cogs and cranks and levers; they are still mentally in the steam-engine era. They cannot imagine the subtlety and sophistication of the great computers which are now leaving the laboratory, some of which may comprise a million circuit elements and be as large as a house—*yet contain practically no moving parts,* though they may carry out a hundred thousand operations a second. The machines we are building now differ in kind as well as degree from all that mankind has ever seen before—and their evolution is barely beginning.

No one can say where it will lead, but glimpsed vaguely in the mists of the future is a dream—I will not say a possibility—which has long been hinted at in most of the religions of the world. Since pattern alone is important, can mind and intelligence exist without matter? In the relationship between, for example, purely electrical entities or packages of radiation? There is some evidence that space itself has a fundamental structure, and could therefore in principle be used as a medium for storing and processing information.

And thus, intelligence, which arose from the interactions of matter and has used it as a vehicle for so many ages, may at last break loose from its origin, as a butterfly from the prisons of its chrysalis. And like the butterfly climbing into the summer sky, it may go on to orders of experience completely beyond the reach of its earlier metamorphoses.

Where are we today in the hierarchy which, ages hence, may culminate in something which only the word "spirit" can describe? Are we the chrysalis, the larva—or merely the unhatched egg?

★   WHICH WAY IS UP?
★

★ WHEN I became amphibious, I never expected that it would cause such confusion among my friends. Yet I can understand their feelings; when one has been writing and talking about space flight for the best part of twenty years, a sudden switch of interest from the other side of the stratosphere to the depths of the sea does seem peculiar. It might be regarded as a serious failure to keep to the point— even a demonstration of a certain lack of stability. So, to put the record straight, I'd like to explain just why it is that I've traded in my space suit for an Aqua-Lung, my telescope for an underwater camera.

The first excuse I give to baffled journalists and lecture chairmen agonizing over their introductions is the economic one; submarine exploration is so much cheaper than space flight. The first round ticket to the Moon is going to cost at least $10 billion if you include research and development. By the end of this century it will be down to a few million— but the complete basic kit needed for skin diving (flippers, face mask and snorkel tube) can be bought for twenty dollars. Which, it can hardly be denied, is a very modest price to pay for admission to a new element.

My second argument is more philosophical: the ocean, surprisingly enough, has many points of similarity to space. Some of these I had guessed even before I first went underwater; others I did not discover until I had been diving for several years, though I do my best to claim that I had anticipated them all.

In their different ways, both sea and space are equally hostile to Man. If we wish to survive in either for any length of time, we have to employ mechanical aids. The diving dress was the prototype of the space suit; the sensations and emotions of a man beneath the sea will have much in common with those of a man beyond the atmosphere.

One of those sensations is weightlessness, and it was this fact, as much as any other, that first got me interested in underwater swimming. Here on the surface of the Earth, it is never possible to escape from gravity. All our lives, we creatures of the land must drag the weight of our bodies around with us, envying the freedom of the birds and clouds.

In a spaceship, however, once the thrust of the rockets has ceased, all weight vanishes, and the effect that this will have upon the human organism has long been the subject of debate among medical men. It has been suggested that "spacesickness" and perhaps total incapacity might result when there is no longer any way of distinguishing between up and down, because both conceptions have lost all meaning.

Something rather like this happens underwater, for gravity plays little part in the lives of fish and other marine creatures. Looking at the matter scientifically, it occurred to me that, if I imitated them, I might discover what it felt like to be a spaceman.

There is no doubt that one of the greatest attractions of skin diving is the sense of freedom in three dimensions that it gives; when your buoyancy is properly neutralized by lead weights, you can float without any effort at any level. If you push against a rock or kick off from the seabed, you will drift slowly until the friction of the water destroys your momentum. Until the first manned satellite is established, this is the nearest we shall know to the conditions that prevail inside a spaceship.

I soon discovered, however, that the analogy was not exact. Though you possess no weight when you are submerged, up and down still exist. Even when the other senses fail, your eyes can give you all the orientation you need. Unless you are swimming after sunset, or in very dirty water, you can always tell the direction from which the light is coming. It may be no more than a vague glow like the first hint of dawn, but it is an unmistakable signpost to the surface.

Well—almost unmistakable, for there are exceptions even to this rule. I was once diving in a somewhat gloomy coral cave whose floor was covered with light sand when I was surprised to see that most of the fish around me were swimming upside down. All the light came from below—and they'd been fooled into thinking that this direction was up.

Men are, on the whole, more intelligent than fish, but here is a case where what counts is instinct, not intelligence. It would seem that as long as the cabin of a space vehicle looked normally orientated to the eye, the danger of vertigo would be greatly reduced, even in the complete absence of gravity. However, if chairs and tables were bolted indiscriminately to all six walls, that would be asking for trouble. Even the most hardened astronaut might soon feel unhappy unless there was a general agreement that a certain direction would be up, and the cabin was designed and used accordingly. (One can picture the warning notices PLEASE DO NOT SIT ON THE CEILING.) Once the eye had been satisfied, its signals would override any messages from other sense organs which were frantically telling the brain that gravity had ceased to exist.

It was Cousteau who coined the phrase "Silent World" to describe the sea, but the description is even more applicable to space. There are a few sounds under water: porpoises squeak, whales groan, shrimp snap their claws. In the vacuum of space, however, no sounds can exist, for there is nothing to transmit them. The only noises that a space traveler will normally hear are those created inside his ship —the whirring of electric motors, the hiss of air pumps, the clank of metal upon metal. These sounds would echo round and round the little world of the ship and would form a continuous background which would be noticed only when there was some change in it. In the same way, an Aqua-Lunger is seldom consciously aware of the bubbling of his exhaust valve—but when it stops he reacts at once, even before he feels the alteration in the airflow.

Very occasionally, a space traveler might hear a noise from the outer world. From time to time particles of meteor dust would hit the hull with enough impact to make an audible sound; on still rarer occasions, when the meteor was a really large one, that sound might be the last thing that the voyager would ever hear.

In space there are no horizons; the questing eye reaches out forever, in all directions, and finds no fixed point at which to rest. For this reason there is also no real sense of distance; in the absence of perspective, it is impossible to judge the remoteness of the stars. They could be pin points of light a few miles away, as indeed the ancients thought they were. The truth is so incredible that the instinct rejects it, and a man midway between the planets might feel that he could reach out and grasp the gleaming sparks around him.

This sense of floating in a void which is not infinite, but merely indefinite, is one that can be captured in the sea under certain conditions. If you dive into deep water and head quickly downward, you can lose all sight of the surface before there is any trace of the bottom. You will then be suspended in a completely featureless blue-green void, and if there are no fish within your field of vision, it is quite impossible to judge how far you can see. Visibility may be a hundred feet—yet you can delude yourself into thinking that you cannot see more than a yard.

This is not a pleasant sensation, and more than once I have been glad to reassure myself, simply by stretching out my hand and looking at my fingers, that I *could* see further than my nose. Whether a similar illusion will arise in space we will not know until we can get a few million miles away from Earth; if it does, then the ocean is one place where we can prepare men to meet it.

Another lesson for space which I have learned from the sea is that the human body is much tougher and more adaptable than anyone could reasonably have expected. Although it is necessary, in a vehicle traveling beyond the atmosphere, to provide complete protection against the vacuum of space by the use of a pressure cabin, I believe that the achievements of today's skin divers have demonstrated that men could withstand even exposure to airless space for appreciable periods of time—a fact which might make all the difference between life and death in an emergency.

This statement will certainly astonish a good many people, especially those who have read science-fiction stories containing gruesome accounts of what happens to space travelers when their ship springs a leak, or is punctured by a meteor. Yet in either of these cases, it would normally take several seconds for the air pressure to drop to zero, *and a skin diver coming up quickly from a depth of only ten feet experiences a greater pressure drop, in a far shorter time, than the occupants of a spaceship would undergo if their vessel was suddenly holed.*

Skin diving has also shown what an extraordinarily long period of time men can exist without breathing, if they have suitable training and preparation. The first time I went underwater, I stayed down all of ten seconds. But as I became more confident, and learned the tricks of the trade, I was able to push my endurance up to three and a half minutes; though this sounds impressive, it is nothing compared with the record, which is now over thirteen minutes.

This has convinced me that trained men, given sufficient warning so that they could prepare themselves, would be able to stand exposures of a minute or so even to the vacuum of space. Recently I had a chance of arguing this point with Major David Simons, the only man who has so far spent more than a day beyond the effective limits of the atmosphere. (During his famous balloon ascent in 1957, he had more than 99 per cent of the atmosphere below him, so that for most physiological purposes he was out in space.) Major Simons was willing to grant me fifteen seconds of consciousness on exposure to vacuum, but considered that death would then follow swiftly because the brain would be deprived of oxygen.

Well, fifteen seconds is a very long time in an emergency, —long enough to get into the next cabin and slam the airtight doors. And I have a hunch that the margin of safety may be better than fifteen seconds, for the human body has so often surprised us in the past by its unexpected powers of adaptation. Not long ago, doctors proved conclusively that a naked diver could not possibly descend a hundred feet without having his lungs crushed by the pressure. Yet the skin-diving record is now 140 feet *without breathing gear*, and there is evidence that some divers have been down 200 feet—a depth at which the pressure on every square foot of the body is over five tons. Yes—the human frame can take a lot of punishment if it has to, and there are occasions when a space pilot may be tougher than his ship.

In the exploration of a new element, psychology is as important as physiology. From my own experience, I'm convinced that underwater exploring inculcates the kind of mental outlook which we shall need in space. It may be summed up as a sense of alertness—a realization that almost anything can happen, and that when it does you've got to be ready for it. This is not a question of being nervous or apprehensive, so much as being prepared, so that you react properly and don't panic. In the sea, panic can be the deadliest of killers, and it needs so little to bring it on—a strange movement glimpsed out of the corner of the eye, a slight malfunctioning of equipment, a shadow crossing the seabed when you know there are no clouds in the sky, a sound in a world which is normally silent. And, above all, an unexpected, purposeful contact when you think you are floating alone in mid-ocean. . . .

There is a test that the Australian Navy used on its frogmen to separate, not the men from the boys, but the men from the supermen. (Readers prone to nightmares had better skip the next two paragraphs.) It consisted of sending a trainee down into the water, at night, with his face mask blacked out so that he was totally blind. A second diver with a sealed-beam searchlight would be in the neighborhood to keep an eye on the victim, who had been instructed to swim back to the surface. This is not difficult, even when you cannot see your way, because it is a simple matter to increase buoyancy and thus go up like a balloon. In this case, however, there was a fiendish complication of which the victim was unaware.

He had been released in the middle of an underwater jungle—a dense forest of kelp. The thin fronds, scores of yards long, formed a close-packed wall around him, and the current carried him steadily toward it. Without the slightest warning, he would hit this floating barrier—and at once the tons of unstable vegetation would collapse, engulfing him (in utter darkness, remember) beneath an animated avalanche of twining tendrils. By the time he had been dug out of this and brought back to the surface, his instructors would know if he'd made the grade.

Anyone who could pass a test like this would be a useful man to have around in one of those typical space emergencies where the atomic pile is about to go out of control, the captain is down with the D.T.'s, the last of the oxygen is leaking through a meteor puncture, and the Thing has broken loose from its cage in the hold.

Talking of Things leads us to another, and somewhat speculative, link between sea and space. Sooner or later, during our exploration of the Universe, we are going to encounter utterly alien forms of life. It does not seem likely that we will meet them on the Moon when we get there in the 1970's, but the first contact may occur on Mars a decade or so later.

There is absolutely no way of guessing what shape extraterrestrial life forms may take; even if we had perfect knowledge of conditions on Mars and Venus (the only planets where protoplasmic life could exist), we would be no nearer to picturing the creatures that might live there. If anyone doubts this, let him ask himself if he could have predicted the elephant, the duck-billed platypus, the giraffe, or Homo sapiens from a geophysical survey of the planet Earth.

Until we reach them—or they reach us—we shall remain in complete ignorance about the creatures which may exist on other planets. Perhaps we may find no more than a few lichens on Mars; perhaps our first encounter with extraterrestrial animals or intelligences may still lie centuries in the future. Yet even now, by sinking down into the sea, we can capture many of the sensations our descendants will know when they set foot upon other planets. Certainly nothing that they will ever meet there can be more fantastic than some of the creatures which inhabit the waters of this world.

This is another reason why underwater exploring is, psychologically, a good preparation for Man's adventure in space—and why, incidentally, it can be a good corrective to the psychotic horror movies which depict all extraterrestrial beings as hideous monsters bent on destruction. Monsters do not exist in Nature, but only in men's minds. I learned this lesson the first time I met a giant manta ray, and I have never forgotten it.

Sometimes known as the devilfish, because of its grotesque batlike shape and the two horns or palps extending on either side of its mouth, the manta is one of the weirdest looking beasts of the sea. When, long before I had dreamed of doing any underwater exploring myself, I saw some of Hans Haas' photos of this strange creature (which can grow up to thirty feet across) I thought I had never seen anything so hideous; its head reminded me strongly of the gargoyles on Notre Dame. Yet five years later, when I encountered one of the great beasts peacefully browsing over a coral reef off the Queensland coast, that initial feeling of repulsion vanished completely. Here, it was true, was something strange and beyond ordinary experience, but it was no longer hideous—it was not even alien. Its fitness of purpose and the grace of its movements as it flapped along the reef, keeping a wary eye on the human invaders of its territory, left little room in my mind for anything except admiration—and a furious rage against those fishermen (above or below the water) who sometimes spear these huge, harmless beasts for their amusement.

To most people, perhaps the most ghastly inhabitant of the sea—the ultimate in creeping, malevolent horror—is the octopus. The very thought of contact with its slimy, sucker-studded tentacles is enough to make them feel physically sick, yet once again this is a reaction founded on ignorance or inspired by stories put out by divers who want to make their job sound even more dangerous than it is. I would not go so far as to say that the octopus is a friendly, attractive beast which no home should be without, but I would claim that almost all one's original revulsion vanishes when one gets to know this talented mollusk. In real life, and not when seen frozen in menace by an imaginative illustrator, the octopus is quite fascinating to watch as it jets across the seabed or slithers briskly from rock to rock, only too anxious to keep out of your way. And its rapid color changes, when it is excited or nervous, are really beautiful.

These examples should be sufficient to prove my point—that there is nothing in the natural world, however strange it may be, that one cannot grow accustomed to. Albert Schweitzer must have had this in mind when he formulated his doctrine of "reverence for life"; it is a creed that a man of sensitivity can learn in the sea as nowhere else—and it is one which mankind must master before it makes contact with other intelligent races in the Universe. I have never been convinced that intelligence comes only in one model—and that that model has two legs, two arms, two eyes and one mouth.

Someday we may encounter representatives of far higher civilizations than ours, who may differ from us as greatly as we differ from the manta or the octopus. And as we have had to overcome color prejudice, so our descendants may have to overcome a much more fundamental *shape* prejudice. The time may come when no well-bred person would dream of remarking that the ambassador from Rigel looks like a cross between a jellyfish and a tarantula (even if he does) or is particularly upset because the members of the Sirian trade delegation have not only three heads but also four sexes.

Fantasy? Of course; the reality of our Universe *is* fantastic. We live in an age when we can keep up with tomorrow —or even today—only by letting our imaginations freewheel anywhere they care to travel, as long as they keep within the bounds of logic and the known laws of Nature.

Yet if we hope to reach the stars, we shall need more than imagination, more than scientific skill. These alone would be useless without the spirit of adventure which conquered our own world in the days when much of this Earth was as mysterious and remote as the planets seem today.

That spirit is not lacking; along all the coasts of the world, boys (and girls) barely in their teens are setting off on sub-aqueous journeys which would have seemed utterly incredible to their grandparents, and which must often terrify their parents. Among those youthful skin divers, the men who will make up the space crews of tomorrow are already learning courage, judgment, self-confidence and those less definable qualities needed by all great explorers.

I began this apologia on a personal note; I would like to end it on one. The parallels between sea and space are sufficiently clear, and there is no need to say any more to prove that underwater exploration has a perfectly logical tie-in with astronautics. Yet logic is never enough; it was Bertrand Russell—somewhat surprisingly—who remarked that the purpose of reason is to give us excuses for doing the things we want to.

In the final analysis, I went undersea because I liked it there, because it opened up to me a new, strange world as fantastic and magical as the one which Alice discovered behind the looking glass. And perhaps I did it because, after hearing people call me a space-travel expert for twenty years, I felt I was getting into a rut. As Hollywood stars know very well, it is fatal to become typed; if you want to progress, to continue your mental and emotional growth, every so often you must surprise yourself (and your friends) by changing the pattern of your life and interests.

Once you are neatly classified and pigeonholed, incapable of any further development, your life is over. You might as well be a stuffed specimen in a museum, completely described by the label tied to your ankle. When there's nothing more to say about you, you're already dead.

I feel very happy to have avoided that fate, but there's one problem that sometimes worries me. What new track do I switch to in 1975?

★ REPORT ON PLANET THREE
★

★ (THE following document, which has just been deciphered for the Interplanetary Archaeological Commission, is one of the most remarkable that has yet been discovered on Mars, and throws a vivid light upon the scientific knowledge and mental processes of our vanished neighbors. It dates from the Late Uranium [i.e. final] Age of the

Martian civilization, and thus was written little more than a thousand years before the birth of Christ.

The translation is believed to be reasonably accurate, though a few conjectural passages have been indicated. Where necessary, Martian terms and units have been converted into their terrestrial equivalents for ease of understanding.—Translator.)

The recent close approach of the planet Earth has once again revived speculations about the possibility of life upon our nearest neighbor in space. This is a question which has been debated for centuries, without conclusive results. In the last few years, however, the development of new astronomical instruments has given us much more accurate information about the other planets. Though we cannot yet confirm or deny the existence of terrestrial life, we now have much more precise knowledge of conditions on Earth, and can base our discussions on a firm scientific foundation.

One of the most tantalizing things about Earth is that we cannot see it when it is closest, since it is then between us and the Sun and its dark side is therefore turned toward us. We have to wait until it is a morning or evening star, and thus a hundred million or more miles away from us, before we can see much of its illuminated surface. In the telescope, it then appears as a brilliant crescent, with its single giant Moon hanging beside it. The contrast in color between the two bodies is striking; the Moon is a pure silvery-white, but the Earth is a sickly blue-green. [The exact force of the adjective is uncertain; it is definitely unflattering. "Hideous" and "virulent" have been suggested as alternatives.—Translator.]

As the Earth turns on its axis—its day is just half an hour shorter than ours—different areas of the planet swing out of darkness and appear on the illuminated crescent. By carrying out observations over a period of weeks, it is possible to construct maps of the entire surface, and these have revealed the astonishing fact that *more than two-thirds of the planet Earth are covered with liquid.*

Despite the violent controversy which has raged over this matter for some centuries, there is no longer any reasonable doubt that this liquid is water. Rare though water now is upon Mars, we have good evidence that in the remote past much of our planet was submerged beneath vast quantities of this peculiar compound; it appears, therefore, that Earth is in a state corresponding to our own world several billion years ago. We have no way of telling how deep the terrestrial "oceans"—to give them their scientific name—may be, but some astronomers have suggested that they are as much as a thousand feet in thickness.

The planet also has a very much more abundant atmosphere than ours; calculations indicate that it is at least ten times as dense. Until quite recently, we had no way of guessing the composition of that atmosphere, but the spectroscope has now solved this problem—with surprising results. The thick gaseous envelope surrounding the Earth contains large amounts of the poisonous and very reactive element oxygen, of which scarcely a trace exists in our own air. Earth's atmosphere also holds considerable quantities of nitrogen and water vapor, which forms huge clouds, often persisting for many days and obscuring large areas of the planet.

Being some 25 per cent nearer the Sun than Mars, Earth is at a considerably higher temperature than our world. Readings taken by thermocouples attached to our largest telescopes reveal intolerable temperatures on its Equator; at higher latitudes, however, conditions are much less extreme and the presence of extensive icecaps at both poles indicates that temperatures there are often quite comfortable. These polar icecaps never melt completely, as do ours during the summer, so they must be of immense thickness.

As Earth is a much larger planet than Mars (having twice our diameter), its gravity is a good deal more powerful. It is, indeed, no less than three times as great, so that a 170-pound man would weigh a quarter of a ton on Earth. This high gravity must have many important consequences, not all of which we can foresee. It would rule out any large forms of life, since they would be crushed under their own weight. It is something of a paradox, however, that Earth possesses mountains far higher than any that exist on Mars; this is probably another proof that it is a young and primitive planet, whose original surface features have not yet eroded away.

Looking at these well-established facts, we can now weigh the prospects for life on Earth. It must be said at once that they appear extremely poor; however, let us be open-minded and prepared to accept even the most unlikely possibilities, as long as they do not conflict with scientific laws.

The first great objection to terrestrial life—which many experts consider conclusive—is the intensely poisonous atmosphere. The presence of such large quantities of gaseous oxygen poses a major scientific problem, which we are still far from solving. Oxygen is so reactive that it cannot normally exist in the free state; on our own planet, for example, it is combined with iron to form the beautiful red deserts that cover so much of the world. It is the absence of these areas which gives Earth its unpleasant greenish hue.

Some unknown process must be taking place on Earth which liberates immense quantities of this gas. Certain speculative writers have suggested that terrestrial life forms may actually release oxygen during the course of their metabolism. Before we dismiss this idea as being too fanciful, it is worth noting that several primitive and now extinct forms of Martian vegetation did precisely this. Nevertheless, it is very hard to believe that plants of this type can exist on Earth in the inconceivably vast quantities which would be needed to provide so much free oxygen. [We know better, of course. All the Earth's oxygen is a by-product of vegetation; our planet's original atmosphere, like that of Mars today, was oxygen-free.—Translator.]

Even if we assume that creatures exist on Earth which can survive in so poisonous and chemically reactive an atmosphere, the presence of these immense amounts of oxygen has two other effects. The first is rather subtle, and has only recently been discovered by a brilliant piece of theoretical research, now fully confirmed by observations.

It appears that at a great altitude in the Earth's atmosphere—some twenty or thirty miles—the oxygen forms a gas known as ozone, containing three atoms of oxygen as compared with the normal molecule's two. This gas, though it exists in very small quantities so far from the ground, has an overwhelmingly important effect upon terrestrial conditions. It almost completely blocks the ultraviolet rays of the Sun, preventing them from reaching the surface of the planet.

This fact alone would make it impossible for the life forms we know to exist on Earth. The Sun's ultraviolet radiation, which reaches the surface of Mars almost unhindered, is essential to our well-being and provides our bodies with much of their energy. Even if we could withstand the corrosive atmosphere of Earth, we should soon perish owing to this lack of vital radiation.

The second result of the high oxygen concentration is even more catastrophic. It involves a terrifying phenomenon, fortunately known only in the laboratory, which scientists have christened "fire."

Many ordinary substances, when immersed in an atmosphere like that of Earth's and heated to quite modest temperatures, begin a violent and continuous chemical reaction which does not cease until they are completely consumed. During the process, intolerable quantities of heat and light are generated, together with clouds of noxious gases. Those who have witnessed this phenomenon under controlled laboratory conditions describe it as quite awe-inspiring; it is certainly fortunate for us that it can never occur on Mars.

Yet it must be quite common on Earth—and no possible form of life could exist in its presence. Observations of the night side of Earth have often revealed bright glowing areas where fire is raging; though some students of the planets have tried, optimistically, to explain these glows as the lights of cities, this theory must be rejected. The glowing regions are much too variable; with few exceptions, they are quite short-lived, and they are not fixed in location. [These observations were doubtless due to forest fires and volcanoes— the latter unknown on Mars. It is a tragic irony of fate that had the Martian astronomers survived a few more thousand years, they *would* have seen the lights of Man's cities. We missed each other in time by less than a millionth of the age of our planets.—Translator.]

Its dense, moisture-laden atmosphere, high gravity and closeness to the Sun make Earth a world of violent climatic extremes. Storms of unimaginable intensity have been observed raging over vast areas of the planet, some of them accompanied by spectacular electrical disturbances, easily detected by sensitive radio receivers here on Mars. It is hard to believe that any form of life could withstand these natural convulsions, from which the planet is seldom completely free.

Although the range of temperatures between the terrestrial winter and summer is not so great as on our world, this is slight compensation for other handicaps. On Mars, all mobile life forms can easily escape the winter by migration. There are no mountains or seas to bar the way; the small size of our world—as compared with Earth—and the greater length of the year make such seasonable movements a simple matter, requiring an average speed of only some ten miles a day. There is no need for us to endure the winter, and few Martian creatures do so.

It must be quite otherwise on Earth. The sheer size of the planet, coupled with the shortness of the year (which only lasts about six of our months) means that any terrestrial beings would have to migrate at a speed of about fifty miles a day in order to escape from the rigors of winter. Even if such a rate could be achieved (and the powerful gravity makes this appear most unlikely) mountains and oceans would create insuperable barriers.

Some writers of "science fiction" have tried to get over this difficulty by suggesting that life forms capable of aerial locomotion may have evolved on Earth. In support of this rather farfetched idea they argue that the dense atmosphere would make flying relatively easy; however, they gloss over the fact that the high gravity would have just the reverse effect. The conception of flying animals, though a charming one, is not taken seriously by any competent biologist.

More firmly based, however, is the theory that if any terrestrial animals exist, they will be found in the extensive oceans which cover so much of the planet. It is believed that life on our own world originally evolved in the ancient Martian seas, so there is nothing at all fantastic about this idea. In the oceans, moreover, the animals of Earth would no longer have to fight the fierce gravity of their planet. Strange though it is for us to imagine creatures which could live in water, it would seem that the seas of Earth may provide a less hostile environment than the land.

Quite recently, this interesting idea has received a setback through the work of the mathematical physicists. Earth, as is well known, has a single enormous Moon, which must be one of the most conspicuous objects in its sky. It is some two hundred times the diameter of even the larger of our two satellites, and though it is at a much greater distance its attraction must produce powerful effects on the planet beneath it. In particular, what are known as "tidal forces" must cause great movements in the waters of the terrestrial oceans, making them rise and fall through distances of many feet.

As a result, all low-lying areas of the Earth must be subjected to twice-daily flooding; in such conditions, it is difficult to believe that any creatures could exist either in land or sea, since the two would be constantly interchanging.

To sum up, therefore, it appears that our neighbor Earth is a forbidding world of raw, violent energies, certainly quite unfitted for any type of life which now exists on Mars. That some form of vegetation may flourish beneath that rain-burdened, storm-tossed atmosphere is quite possible; indeed, many astronomers claim to have detected color changes in certain areas which they attribute to the seasonal growth of plants.

As for animals—this is pure speculation, all the evidence being against them. If they exist at all, they must be extremely powerful and massively built to resist the high gravity, probably possessing many pairs of legs and capable only of slow movement. Their clumsy bodies must be covered with thick layers of protective armor to shield them from the many dangers they must face, such as storms, fire and corrosive atmosphere. In view of these facts, the question of *intelligent* life on Earth must be regarded as settled. We must resign ourselves to the idea that we are the only rational beings in the Solar System.

For those romantics who still hope for a more optimistic answer, it may not be long before Planet Three reveals its last secrets to us. Current work on rocket propulsion has shown that it is quite possible to build a space craft which can escape from Mars and head across the cosmic gulf toward our mysterious neighbor. Though its powerful gravity would preclude a landing (except by radio-controlled robot vehicles) we could orbit Earth at a low altitude and thus observe every detail of its surface from little more than a millionth of our present distance.

Now that we have at last released the limitless energy of the atomic nucleus, we may soon use this tremendous new power to escape the bonds of our native world. Earth and its giant satellite will be merely the first celestial bodies our future explorers will survey. Beyond them lie . . .

[Unfortunately, the manuscript ends here. The remainder has been charred beyond decipherment, apparently by the thermonuclear blast that destroyed the Imperial Library, together with the rest of Oasis City. It is a curious coincidence that the missiles which ended Martian civilization were launched at a classic moment in human history. Forty million miles away, with slightly less advanced weapons, the Greeks were storming Troy.—Translator.]

★ QUESTION TIME
★

   ★ WHEN I started lecturing in the United States I solemnly vowed that here, for a change, would be one visiting Englishman who would *not* write a book about his attempts to bring culture and learning to darkest America. That promise still stands, if only for the reason that after a hundred appearances in every part of the country I can't always remember where I've been. (Indeed, not long ago I flatly denied ever visiting one large city in which I'd lectured just three weeks before.) But like the young lady who shrugged off an inexplicable baby on the grounds that, after all, it was only a very small one, I hope I can be permitted this brief relapse.

It is more than twenty years, I am somewhat horrified to discover, since I began lecturing on space flight. In my 1958 season, thanks to the unexpected co-operation of the Kremlin, I started my tour not merely one up but two up on my audiences. Both Sputniks were circling the Earth when I delivered my first talk on satellites; gone forever, consequently, was the opinionated little man in the front row who was quite sure that space travel was impossible—because no one had ever done it before. Sometimes I miss him; it used to be more fun when there was at least one person in the audience who thought I was crazy, and didn't hesitate to say so.

The organizations I've addressed during my tours cover almost the entire spectrum of American life—universities, women's clubs, businessmen's associations, YMCA's, synagogues, public libraries. The qualifying "almost" is inserted because there is one type of audience I have not so far met. I'm still awaiting an invitation from the warden of Sing Sing to address his charges; but perhaps the subject of space flight is considered too escapist.

Such varying audiences naturally react in very different ways to the prospect of being shot out into the cosmic void. My younger hearers, not surprisingly, are the more enthusiastic; older groups manage to restrain their enthusiasm and often regard the coming Age of Space as something to be endured rather than enjoyed.

The first platform peril which every speaker has to face is, of course, the chairman, whose introduction can all too often be the kiss of death. (As per the fine example quoted, in its entirety, by Stephen Potter: "It's often said that Englishmen have no sense of humor. Just wait until you have heard Mr. Potter.") On the whole I have been fortunate; at least I have never yet been introduced as someone else. But several times the chairman has got my name partly wrong; on one occasion I was introduced to a surprised audience as "Mr. *Adam* Clarke," and spent the first ten minutes of my lecture in a somewhat distracted mood, wondering whose Freudian slip was showing.

Though audience reactions vary greatly, the questions I am asked after the lecture do not. I can usually tell, before my interrogator has spoken more than a dozen words, just what problem is worrying him, and automatically switch the appropriate sound track into place. There are times when I have grown so tired of such hoary old faithfuls as "What about meteors?" "Are cosmic rays dangerous?" that I've felt like giving a prize to anyone who can think of a new question about space flight. For a really good one, I might even waive my lecture fee. [Important! Mr. Clarke is, of course, only joking—W. Colston Leigh, Inc.]

The problem which still seems to worry many people is the one which is basic to the whole conception of space flight. How, they often ask, can a rocket work out there in the vacuum of space, where there is nothing for it to push against?

After trying various answers over the past couple of decades, I've finally settled on this one, which has the merit (unlike many scientific "explanations") of not being simplified to the point of inaccuracy. It's quite correct, I start by admitting, that any propulsive device has to have something to push on. A ship pushes on the sea, an automobile pushes on the land. If you were out in space, surrounded by light-years of nothingness, you coud not move an inch without having some material substance to thrust against. *You have, therefore, to carry such a substance with you.*

It could be any material whatsoever; one day it may be something as cheap and simple as water. At the moment, however, it happens to be the rocket fuel itself—the scores or hundreds of tons of liquids which comprise more than 90 per cent of the mass of any space vehicle. This is what the rocket pushes against; the tremendously violent combustion (someone once described a rocket launching as a "controlled catastrophe") blasts the heavy fuel in one direction, and the much lighter vehicle therefore builds up an even greater speed in the other.

The emptiness of space—a conception which appears to be universally appreciated, even though its implications are not always understood—sometimes prompts another query, from those who do not grasp the fundamental difference between radio and sound waves. Since sound cannot pass through a vacuum, I am occasionally asked how it is possible for a space ship to communicate with Earth.

Perhaps the best answer to this question is given by the Sun. The rays bringing its light and heat to us differ from radio waves only by being very much shorter, and they reach us without difficulty across 93,000,000 miles of empty space. The recent development of radio astronomy (that is, the observation of the heavenly bodies by means of the radio waves they emit) has given an even clearer proof that radio can span not merely interplanetary, but interstellar gulfs. Indeed, it now appears that our radio telescopes can see further into space than our optical ones, for the waves they operate with are less easily absorbed in the great dust and gas clouds —the debris of creation—which swirl between the stars. For as long as we can foresee, men will be able to send their messages far ahead of their ships.

The two questions I have just repeated have this in common: they are quite sensible ones, but they could not have been asked by anyone with even an elementary understanding of science. The principle of action and reaction was enunciated by Newton three hundred years ago; the fact that radio waves could pass through a vacuum was understood even before Hertz first produced them in 1888. At the risk of laboring a point which has been somewhat heavily plugged since S-day burst bleeping upon the world, we have now reached the stage when some knowledge of basic science is as necessary for everyday life as the ability to read and write. The commonly heard cry, "We need more scientists!" is an oversimplification, and perhaps a dangerous one. What we *really* need are more educated men—and in the future anyone who is totally ignorant of science is, frankly, uneducated. And if, like some people today, he boasts about his ignorance, he will be in precisely the same position as those illiterate medieval barons who proudly claimed that figuring and copying were jobs they left to their clerks.

It by no means follows, however, that people who have never had a formal scientific education cannot hope to understand how satellites and spaceships work. Astronautics is based on familiar physical principles; the behavior of rockets and space vehicles can be related in a direct and simple fashion to the movements of objects in everyday life. They don't defy common sense in the lighthearted manner of neutrinos, mesons, electrons and the other particles of the subatomic world.

It's an interesting challenge to the lecturer to put across the basic principles of space flight to an entirely nontechnical audience, and a matter of great satisfaction to watch the dawning comprehension on the faces of people who were convinced that they couldn't understand what it was all about. (Not that I can always claim to have succeeded; at least twice I've been deflated by: "Thank you for such a fascinating talk, Mr. Clarke. Of course, it was right over *my* head.")

The most interesting and stimulating questions I am asked by my audiences are not, however, scientific or technical ones. They concern matters of philosophy, politics and religion, and often reveal very clearly the climate of opinion on the subject of space travel. It is hardly surprising that from October 4, 1957, until the first American satellite was launched on February 1, 1958, one of the commonest questions was an anguished, "Why didn't *we* do it first?"

I don't want to get involved here with the answers to that *cri de coeur*, and will make a swift detour round it to deal with a closely allied subject. Whenever the comparison between U.S. and Russian rocketry comes up, someone will inevitably bring up the argument that the Russians received great (perhaps decisive) help from German rocket scientists. This pathetic apology still dies hard; I find it particularly exasperating because it is based not upon ignorance (which can be excused) but upon stupidity (which cannot).

One would have thought that even before Dr. Wernher von Braun's team launched Explorer I most people who read the newspapers would have known that the leading German rocket experts had come to the United States, which should have given this country a decided advantage over the Russians. And in fact the Russians never obtained more than a very small handful of top rocket scientists, all of whom have now returned to Germany and *none of whom had any direct part in the Sputnik program.* The Russians, like everyone else, learned all that they could from wartime German research; thereafter their own very competent scientists did the rest. The fact that they achieved so much *without* the German talent available (and, some would argue, frustrated) in the United States makes their accomplishments all the more remarkable.

It is an interesting—and possibly significant—fact that nowhere have I come across any religious opposition to the idea of space travel. To one questioner who asked me, "Does space flight agree with God's plan for Man?" I had to confess that I was not privy to the details of this fascinating thesis. I could merely point out that there seemed no fundamental difference between exploring the Universe and exploring the Earth. No doubt there were people in the past who believed it was impious to discover new lands, on the grounds that what was good enough for their grandfathers, etc. But I could not imagine any citizen of so recently settled a country as the United States supporting this argument; if he believed in it, he had no right to be alive.

As far as Catholics are concerned this matter is presumably settled. Pope Pius XII, in the course of a brilliant address to the 1956 International Astronautical Congress in Rome, made the point that now that Man has discovered the means of getting into space, he would be failing to fulfill his God-given potentialities if he did not do so. It is hard to believe that anyone, whatever his religious faith, can seriously disagree with this argument.

At the same time, it is quite clear that many people realize

—if only subconsciously—that space travel is going to give the human race some considerable shocks in the psyche. It will complete the process of shrinking the Earth to insignificance—a process which has been underway since the invention of the telescope and the rise of modern astronomy. But until today, appreciation of our planet's place in the hierarchy of the Universe has been purely intellectual, not emotional. I well remember the slightly stunned reaction of a Dallas audience to a rocket photo showing the whole of Texas; this will be nothing to the feelings of all mankind when, through space-borne TV eyes, it watches the entire Earth dwindle among the stars—and at last looks for it in vain.

That this immense revolution in thought and outlook will be upon us in little more than a decade—certainly no more than a generation—was the main theme of my talks. We are living, I told audiences from New Hampshire to New Mexico, in a moment unique in all history—the last days of Man's existence as a citizen of a single planet. What is happening now is nothing less than the next stage in evolution, comparable to the time, perhaps a billion years ago, when life came out of the sea and conquered the land. This was an analogy which I used even in Tennessee, conscious though I was there of the disapproving ghost of William Jennings Bryan. Unfortunately I did not know at the time that this idea had been most beautifully expressed half a century ago by Tsiolkovsky, the great Russian pioneer of astronautics: "The Earth is the cradle of Mankind—but you cannot live in a cradle forever."

That so many of my listeners accepted this challenge with zest I found very encouraging. Indeed, not a few were somewhat upset because I limited my modest speculations to the other eight planets of *this* sun. The thought of being confined to the Solar System—a mere 7,400,000,000 miles in diameter—appeared to give them acute claustrophobia and they wanted to know what hope there was of reaching the planetary systems of other stars—and, in particular, of exceeding the speed of light so that journeys could be carried out in a reasonable length of time. My reply to this question (which cropped up in about 50 per cent of my lectures) was that it appeared virtually certain that neither we nor anything else could ever travel faster than light—but that this doesn't rule out interstellar exploration. It will merely make it time-consuming.

One of the most difficult problems which any lecturer on astronautics has to face is that of giving good advice to eager youngsters anxious to build and shoot rockets. It is necessary to tell them—disappointing thought it may be—that under no circumstances should they set up private proving grounds. Such activities can be fatal as well as illegal. Studying hard to earn a degree in engineering or physics is rather less glamorous than producing spectacular explosions or launching reluctant mice into the empyrean, but in the long run it gets you much further. The first man to step out upon the surface of the Moon will have a master's degree in at least one science.

This fact is certainly not realized by the thousands of hopefuls who have—more or less seriously—volunteered for flights into space. At the Army Ballistic Missiles Agency, Huntsville, Alabama, where the Redstone, Jupiter C and Jupiter rockets were built, I was told that such applications frequently conclude with the P.S.: "Please do not let my wife know I have written to you." The general who passed this top-secret piece of information on to me also gave some other news which I consider an even more significant sign of the times. Volunteering for space travel seemed safe enough a few years ago—but now quite a few people are writing in, with every sign of anxiety, to withdraw their earlier applications. . . .

One frankly disturbing feature of my question periods was the interest still shown in flying saucers. I had been optimistic enough to suppose that this subject had now died a natural death; yet it cropped up at almost every session. Since dealing adequately with Unidentified Flying Objects would have required an entire lecture in itself, I usually confined myself to describing some of the half dozen I've seen, and then giving their ridiculously simple explanations.* My pleas for sanity and skepticism in this matter, however, were often not well received by the devotees of this new religion. On one occasion a lady from the audience asked me if I believed that those who claimed to have met men from flying saucers were liars. She sat down rather abruptly when I re-

* See "Things in the Sky" (page 148).

plied, "Yes, madam"; not until a little later did the chairman gleefully inform me that her husband had authored one of the best known of the sacred writings.

Lecturing is not a one-way process; a good audience gives as well as takes, and often a remark will come from the floor which may throw a completely new light upon some idea which the speaker thought he had fully examined. This is an unexpected and welcome bonus to be added to the satisfaction of establishing rapport with a body of interested listeners. The last time this happened to me I had been describing how future generations would first explore the planets and then shape them with the tools of nuclear power so that they would become homes for civilizations as unimagined today as the United States woud have been to the men of the Middle Ages. The picture I had painted of our descendants spreading out from their parent world clearly made a deep impression on one young lady in my audience, for during the question period she rose to ask if I thought that Earth would ever become a kind of ghost town. . . . Somehow this remark has haunted me ever since—perhaps because I have a feeling that one day it may come perfectly true.

Quite a different—though in its way equally memorable—reaction was provoked in a New England college by the remark with which I usually conclude my addresses to younger audiences. After giving them a provisional timetable for the rate of interplanetary exploration, I try to bring home to them what it will mean by this prophecy: "Many of you here in this room may have grandchildren who will not be born on Earth."

This exit line usually produces the desired impact, but in at least one case it failed completely. One young aristocrat in the audience was heard to remark to his neighbor, with Olympian self-assurance, "*My* grandchildren will be born in Boston."

This, needless to say, is not a typical response to the challenge of the future; I would soon have to shut up shop if it were—and so, for that matter, would the United States. I am sure that it is more than counterbalanced by the positive reactions of those forward-looking youngsters upon whom all our tomorrows depend. Sometimes one can recognize them, but those I should really like to meet I shall probably never know, even though they may have sat in the front row (and probably did).

By this time I must have lectured to some tens of thousands of teen-agers, and the laws of chance make it virtually certain that many of them will play important roles in the conquest of space. More than a few will one day walk upon the dusty surface of the Moon, or later still hear the whistle of the thin Martian atmosphere building up outside the walls of their descending ship. And sometimes I wonder how many times my words may have started men along paths that, twenty or thirty years from now, will lead them to strange and lonely deaths, far from their native world.

For the freedom of the Universe is the greatest prize which human hands have ever reached out to grasp; and like all prizes, money alone is not enough to purchase it. Perhaps it is well that I cannot see the futures of those young explorers I unknowingly meet, and must scan their eager faces as vainly as did the poet at Ludlow Fair. Like those Shropshire Lads of a vanished century, many will never grow old, but will "carry back bright to the coiner the mintage of Man." They are the ones who will pay the price for the conquest of space—the price that will be remembered when the billions of dollars and rubles are meaningless entries in dustry ledgers.

★   THINGS IN THE SKY
 ★
   ★ DURING a recent lecture tour of the United States I was astonished (and disturbed) by the continuing extreme interest in "flying saucers." I had been optimistic enough to assume that everyone was as bored with them as I was—but no; they cropped up in at least 50 per cent of the question periods. And although enthusiasm for aerial crockery rises to a sharp peak in the region of California, it is still rampant on both sides of the Atlantic. Indeed, on my last transit through England I recklessly jeopardized my place on future Honours Lists by getting into a brisk argument on the subject with Royalty.

The reason why I don't believe in flying saucers (few of which are saucer-shaped, anyway) is that I've seen far too many. And so will any person of normal eyesight during the course of a few years, if he bothers to look at the sky at all.

Perhaps I had better amplify that statement, and it might also be a good idea to replace the emotion-laden term "flying saucer" with the less controversial one, "unidentified flying object" (U.F.O.). The point I wish to make is that the sky contains an almost endless variety of peculiar sights and objects, only a few of which any one person is ever likely to encounter in a lifetime. Yet any averagely observant person is bound to see some of them, and not knowing their explanation may be misled into thinking he's seen something incredible—instead of merely unfamiliar.

Let me give an example which may seem a little far-fetched, but which makes my point perfectly. Suppose you are completely ignorant of meteorological phenomena, and live in a country where it never rains. Then one day you step out of doors—and there is a huge semicircular arch spanning half the sky. It is so geometrically perfect that you feel it must be artificial, yet it is obviously miles across, and it is beautifully colored in reds, blues, yellows, greens.

Well, if you had never seen one before, what would you make of a rainbow? It no longer creates the slightest surprise, because it is so familiar; and we, unlike our ancestors, have no need to invent supernatural explanations for it. Reason has told us what it is, and there would be many fewer U.F.O.'s around today if reason—or even common sense—was in better supply.

To demonstrate this, I'll describe some of the odd sights I've seen in the heavens, all of them during daylight and under conditions of good visibility. The first was over London on a bright Sunday afternoon, more than twenty years ago. It must have been a Sunday, for that was the only time I had for long walks through the city.

Somewhere north of Oxford Street, I came across a group of people staring at the sky. Following their gaze, I was surprised to see two tiny black dots or disks, very close together, at a great but quite unguessable height above the city. Balloons? I asked myself. No—they don't travel in pairs. And these dots were motionless, despite the fact that a strong wind was blowing. I looked at them for a long time without being able to resolve the mystery; then, having nothing better to do, I started to walk in the general direction of the zoo, above which the objects were floating. (This, by the way, is what the detective-story writers call a Misleading Clue; the London Zoological Gardens had nothing to do with the matter.)

Before you read any further, I would like you to make a determined attempt at explaining this incident. And when I give the simple answer, please don't say in disgust, "Is *that* all there was to it?" Remember Sherlock Holmes' sour remark to Dr. Watson, when that paragon of unsocialized medicine commented on the obviousness of some mystery which Holmes had just solved. Not being a member of the Baker Street Irregulars, I can't quote chapter and verse, but the reprimand ran somewhat in this fashion: "It's always obvious to you, Watson, *after* I've explained it."

Well, the twin disks floating high above London turned out to be not two objects, but one—a box kite at an altitude which must have been at least a mile. It was so high that its shape was quite unrecognizable; the framework could not be seen at all, while the silk-covered ends had lost all squareness and appeared as disks or spheres. Never before or since have I seen a kite at such an altitude; the elderly gentleman who was controlling it from Regent's Park was operating a reel like a big-game fisherman's, and when he finally brought the thing to earth it looked like a half-scale model of the Wright biplane.

If you think that one was too easy, let us move on to number two. This was on the other side of the world—in Brisbane, state capital of Queensland. I was in an office overlooking the city (arguing, if I remember correctly, with a customs inspector about import licenses) and it was late in the afternoon. The sun was low on the horizon—and moving slowly above it from north to south was a line of brilliant silver disks. They looked like metallic mirrors, and they were oscillating or flip-flopping with a regular seesaw motion. Once again, I could not guess their size or distance; they were so bright and tiny against the darkening sky that it was also impossible to decide their shape, but they gave the impression of being ellipses. I don't mind admitting that in the few minutes before they came closer I felt myself wondering if the Martian invasion had started; this was the only time I have ever seen a fleet of textbook flying saucers.

In this case, the explanation turned out to be something I already knew—and didn't believe. Many U.F.O. sightings (including one which is the subject of a celebrated and authentic film) were due, I'd read, to birds reflecting sunlight under unusual conditions of illumination. This theory seemed so absurd that I had dismissed it contemptuously; but it is perfectly correct. The lights I saw flipping across Brisbane were nothing more than seagulls, the undersurfaces of their wings acting like mirrors. Though I have lived beside the sea for a quarter of my life, and am doing so now, this is the only time I have ever witnessed this phenomenon, and I should never have credited it without the evidence of my own eyes. The effect of oscillating metallic disks was absolutely realistic; it would have fooled anyone.

The only U.F.O. that has ever given me the queasy, yet at the same time exhilarating, sensation of being in the presence of the unknown and the inexplicable also occurred in Australia. Perhaps the spectacular surroundings contributed to the impact, for I was standing in Sydney Harbour, immediately beneath the piers of the world's most impressive bridge. (Sorry, San Francisco: size and grace, I'll grant you, but for monumental, built-for-eternity grandeur, nothing can touch Sydney's steel rainbow.)

It was a beautiful, sunny day, and I was looking across the waters of the harbor toward the city, most of which lay framed within that tremendous arch. A strong breeze was sending half a dozen sailing boats scudding over the blue waters, and was also driving a few clouds low across the city. But suddenly I realized, with a distinct prickling at the back of the neck, that there was one exception. A single cloud, darker and more compact than its fellows, was floating *completely motionless*, and quite isolated from any buildings, a hundred feet or so above the roof tops.

It was a couple of miles away, and though I stared at it for a good ten minutes it refused to give up its secret. It simply sat in the sky, defying the wind, while all the other clouds went racing past it. There was nothing to do but to hurry back to the apartment and collect a pair of binoculars, hoping that the apparition wouldn't vanish during my absence.

Luckily, it was still there when I returned; through the

glasses I could see that it was a hundred feet or so downwind of a tall smokestack, and though there was no visible connection between the two, it was obviously produced by material streaming from this chimney, and condensing as it cooled off. Everyone is familiar with the way in which hot steam leaves the spout of a kettle as an invisible gas, and appears a fraction of an inch away in a mist of water droplets. This must have been a similar phenomenon, on a slightly larger scale. The gas, vapor or whatever it was pouring from the chimney condensed for a few seconds as it flowed along the wind, then dispersed again to produce the illusion of an unmoving cloud. In the binoculars it looked rather like a banner flying without benefit of flagpole—or, rather, mysteriously separated from it by a hundred feet of space. Even after I'd worked out the explanation, it was a distinctly uncanny sight.

This strange cloud in the Antipodes brings me naturally to another which I once saw much nearer home, above the farm in the west of England where I spent most of my childhood. On this occasion the explanation was immediate and obvious, if you knew the answer—and utterly unguessable if you did not. That many people don't is proved by the fact that one book on flying saucers has made great play of an identical sighting.

Across twenty or thirty years, some of the details are now blurred in my memory, but I am fairly sure that it was early on a bright spring morning, with the dew fresh upon the ground. A gentle wind was blowing, and it was carrying overhead something which I can best describe as an aerial jellyfish. Sometimes it was almost invisible as it turned and twisted in the breeze; at other times the sunlight glanced from its translucent material, so that it looked like a milk-white ghost as it drifted down the sky, being torn apart by the winds even as it moved. I never saw its like again, though it is one of Nature's commoner marvels, familiar enough to those who do not spend their lives locked up in cities.

This silken cloud is something that has baffled mankind for centuries, and even within the last few years it has given rise to the most absurd speculations about the physiology of extraterrestrial visitors. But it is actually the product of a very humble terrestrail creature—the spider. Most young spiders begin their careers as aeronauts, spinning out long threads known as gossamer, which drag them up into the sky on rising air currents. (There is no such thing, incidentally, as a specific gossamer spider; almost all spiders emigrate by air.) On rare occasions, usually in the late summer, the countless threads intertwine to form evanescent clouds, which assume the most extraordinary appearances as the sunlight catches them; when the spiders eventually descend, acres of ground may be covered with their discarded parachutes.

Of all my U.F.O.'s, the most beautiful occurred during the war. The time was the summer of 1942, the place a radar station on the east coast of England. It was a perfect, cloudless afternoon—and extremely peaceful, for the blitz was over and the V-weapons had yet to come. If you searched carefully, you could see the pale crescent of the Moon, nearing its first quarter, looking lost and lonely in the daylight sky.

And once you had found the Moon, you could hardly miss what was close beside it—a brilliant, pure white point of light, shining steadily as a star, where no star could be in the sundrenched sky. Compared with the pallid lunar crescent, it was almost dazzlingly bright, a fraction of a degree away from the Moon, and apparently motionless with respect to it. However, after you had been watching for about ten minutes, you would have noticed that it was moving very slowly toward the Moon—until at last, an hour or so after the first sighting, it finally reached the edge of the chalky lunar disk and merged into it.

The whole sequence of events occupied most of the afternoon, and, as I had an astronomical telescope with me on the station, the conduct of the war was suspended while all the operators and radar mechanics had a close-up view of something which I do not think they will ever forget—and which, if they had seen it for the first time a few years later, they would very likely have interpreted as a flying saucer making a landing on the Moon.

This U.F.O. brings us into the realm of astronomy. When I used the phrase "shining steadily as a star where no star could be" I was technically correct, but deliberately misleading. No stars are bright enough to be seen in the daylight sky, but there is one planet brilliant enough to challenge the Sun. This is Venus, who is easily visible during daytime for the greater part of every year, if you know exactly where to look for her. All down the centuries people ignorant of astronomy have suddenly spotted her in daylight and raised a great hulla-baloo, unaware of the fact that they were seeing as commonplace a celestial object as the Moon. (Incidentally, a surprising number of people don't realize that the Moon is visible during the day—still less Venus!)

The sight I observed from the radar station was one of the most striking of astronomical phenomena, and not a particularly rare one. (It occurred twice in 1958.) In the course of its movement round the Earth, the Moon is continually getting between us and the other heavely bodies, partially or wholly hiding them from us. When this occurs with respect to the Sun, we call it a solar eclipse; when the Moon passes in front of a planet or star, it is known as an occultation.

What I have described was an occultation of Venus, seen during the daytime. Though both bodies were moving, most of the apparent motion was due to the Moon in its path around the Eearth. About an hour later, Venus emerged from the other side of the Moon and was shining just as brightly as ¹⁻fore.

At this point, I would like to pause for a summing up. Even these few examples collected by one not-very-observant sky-gazer over a period of some twenty years show how extremely easy it is to misinterpret quite ordinary objects when they are seen under unusual conditions. And unless one can arrive at an explanation at the time, there is often no hope of settling the matter at a later date; it remains an unsolved and unsolvable mystery. A perfect example of this was provided a few years ago when an agitated gentleman phoned the police late one night with the news that a flying saucer was racing round his back garden, spitting sparks and flames. When the skeptical cops arrived it was still performing, and after a brief chase they managed to capture it. In a million years, no one—but no one—would guess what it turned out to be. Somebody had been burning trash in a nearby garden, and in the rubbish was an old golf ball. Now a golf ball is highly combustible, and its tightly wound rubber bands contain a great deal of energy—all of which comes out when they start to burn, with the result that the thing takes off like a rocket. Try it one night if you want to scare the neighbors.

Nothing that has so far been said either proves or disproves the existence of genuine, 100 per cent flying saucers from outer space; it merely indicates the need for extreme care in coming to conclusions about peculiar objects seen in the sky. Many U.F.O.'s have been reported by apparently reliable observers which are quite inexplicable in terms of current knowledge—but even this does not prove that they are necessarily the products of intelligence, terrestrial or otherwise. For there is now no doubt that when Nature *really* tries, she can produce "spaceships" that would satisfy the most exacting requirements.

Here is the proof: I am quoting from the May, 1916, issue of *The Observatory,* a scientific journal published by the world's leading astronomical organization, the Royal Astronomical Society. The date—1916—is important, but the description is of an event which occurred more than thirty years before, on the night of November 17, 1882.

The writer was a well-known British astronomer, Walter Maunder, then on the staff of the Greenwich Observatory. He had been asked to describe the most remarkable sight he had ever seen during his many years of observing the heavens, and he recalled that soon after sunset on that November night in 1882 he had been on the roof of the observatory, looking across London, when:

A great circular disc of greenish light suddenly appeared low down in the East-North-East, as though it had just risen, and moved across the sky, as smoothly and steadily as the Sun, Moon, stars and planets move, but nearly a thousand times as quickly. The circularity of its shape was merely the effect of foreshortening, for as it moved it lengthened out, and when it crossed the meridian and passed just above the Moon its form was almost that of a very elongated ellipse, and various observers spoke of it as "cigar-shaped," "like a torpedo" . . . had the incident occurred a third of a century later, beyond doubt everyone would have selected the same simile—it would have been *"just like a Zeppelin."* [My italics]

Remember that Maunder was writing this in 1916, when Zeppelins were very much in the news—even more so than spaceships are today!

Since hundreds of observers all over England and Europe

witnessed this object, reasonably accurate figures for its height, size and speed were obtained. It was 133 miles above the Earth, moving at 10 miles a second—and must have been at least 50 miles in length.

What was it? No one could have given a full answer to that question in 1882, but today we can do so with complete confidence. The solution follows from a clue which I have deliberately omitted; the object was seen during a violent auroral display, and was undoubtedly part of it.

We now know that auroras are caused by streams of electrified particles shot out of the Sun, which cross space and eventually enter the Earth's atmosphere. Here they produce a type of fluorescence much like that which lights up our neon tubes and gas-discharge lamps. Billions of years before Broadway, Nature was hanging her illuminated signs in the polar skies.

Though the Sun is the original source of the energy, our planet is responsible for the strange shapes which the aurora assumes—its ever-changing streamers, curtains and rays. For the Earth's very weak but far-ranging magnetic field, extending thousands of miles out into space, has a focusing effect on these streams of particles, concentrating them at the poles. It makes them paint pictures on the sky, as very similar beams and magnetic fields produce images on the screens of our TV sets.

And sometimes, surprising though it seems, Nature with her 93,000,000-mile-long TV tube can create apparently symmetrical, sharp-edged objects moving steadily across the heavens. (Maunder specifically states that the phenomenon he observed "appeared to be a definite body.") This seems much more remarkable to me than any mere spaceship, but the facts are beyond dispute. Observation of the "torpedo" through the spectroscope proved its auroral nature, and as it passed across Europe it slowly began to break up. The cosmic TV tube went out of focus.

It may be argued that this weird—possibly unique—event cannot account for the hard core of unexplained U.F.O.'s, many of which have been observed in the daytime, when the faint light of the aurora is invisible. Yet I have a hunch that there is a remote connection, and this hunch is based upon a new science which has developed during the last few years, largely under the impetus of missile and nuclear research.

This science—take a deep breath—is magnetohydrodynamics. You'll be hearing a lot more of it in the future, for it's one of the keys to space exploration as well as atomic power. But it concerns us here only because it deals with the movement of electrified gases in magnetic fields—with the sort of thing, in fact, which startled Mr. Maunder and a few thousand other people in 1882.

Today we call these objects "plasmoids." (A lovely word, that; can't you see the title from some he-man's magazine of the Space Age: "I Was Pursued by Plutonian Plasmoids"?) They've been known for quite a while, in the form of one of the most baffling phenomena in the whole of Nature—ball lightning, which is something no one would believe without overwhelming evidence. During thunderstorms, brilliantly glowing spheres are sometimes seen rolling along the ground or moving slowly through the air. Occasionally they explode with great violence, and so until recently have all the theories put forward to explain them. But now we have been able to make small versions—baby plasmoids—in the laboratory; and there have been horrid rumors that the Russians are trying to develop them as weapons.

I have never seen ball lightning and am no means sure that I want to, at least at close quarters. However, with this example of the fantastic tricks natural forces can play, it would be very unwise to argue that even the most impressive U.F.O. *must* be artificial. In fact, a good working rule for U.F.O. observers is: It's not a spaceship unless you can read the Mars registration plate.

Of course, some people claim to have done a good deal better than this, but luckily I am not concerned here with the more extreme aberrations of the human mind. The saucer mania of our age will provide a fascinating study for future psychologists; I find it not amusing but saddening. I could hardly raise a smile when a good lady in Pennsylvania recently attacked me for disbelieving in flying saucers, giving as evidence the fact that they were continually landing in her garden. They made, she added, quite a lot of noise—though the only sound she had definitely identified was "a beautiful, long-drawn-out hallelujah. . . ."

Since one can never rule out all possibilities, there must always remain the faint chance that some U.F.O.'s are visitors from elsewhere, though the evidence against this is so overwhelming that it would require an article much longer than this to give it in detail. And if this verdict disappoints you, I can offer what seems to me very adequate compensation.

If you keep looking at the sky, before much longer you *will* see a genuine spaceship.

But it will be one of ours.

Postscript

Since writing the above, I have seen the finest—and most "classical"—flying saucer of my life. On October 17, 1958, I was aboard KLM Flight 826, coming up the coast of Italy on a bright but somewhat hazy afternoon. We were at about 10,000 feet, en route for Geneva, and the ground was clearly visible at the time (around 2 P.M.).

I was looking down at the coastline almost immediately beneath us, waiting for Naples and Vesuvius to come into view, when I became aware that a brilliant oval of light was keeping pace with the aircraft a few thousand feet below. It appeared to be quite solid, though its edges were hazy and seemed to pulsate slightly; they also had a bluish tinge rather like that of a mercury arc. It was impossible to judge its size or distance, but I had the impression that the object was halfway between the aircraft and the ground. Sometimes it was so brilliant that it hurt the eye to look at it directly.

It was in view for a good ten minutes, keeping station beneath us, and for long periods of time it was remarkably constant both in shape and size. Apart from the occasional quivering of its edge, there was no way of telling that it was not a solid disk; it completely masked the ground beneath. Several of my fellow passengers were busy photographing it, and I am quite sure that they are now proudly showing *genuine* flying saucer photos to their friends.

I must confess that had I caught only a glimpse of this apparition I should have been quite baffled; as it was, I was able to keep it in sight until it disintegrated and slowly faded from view, like a cloud breaking up beneath the Sun. By that time there was no question of its identity.

It was a mock sun, or "sun dog," caused by the presence of an invisible layer of ice crystals between the aircraft and the ground. They are fairly common, though this is the first I have ever seen. The ice crystals act as tiny mirrors, each reflecting an image of the Sun; the combination of myriads form the brilliant disk which, being a reflection, appeared to follow the aircraft. Dr. D. H. Menzel's book *Flying Saucers* has a fine photograph of a mock sun as its frontispiece; the one I observed was more sharp-edged and must have been formed in an unusually stable layer of air, in which the vast majority of ice crystals had almost the same orientation.

★ THE MEN ON THE MOON
★

★ THOUGH whole books have been written about the practical problems involved in colonizing the Moon, there is one aspect of life on our satellite which has been largely overlooked, perhaps because everyone has taken it for granted. It is an aspect which will, in fact, become important long before the first lunar landings take place, for as high-definition photographs accumulate from our rocket probes, millions of square miles of hitherto unknown territory will be dumped into the laps of geographers, scientists —and UN delegates. Sometime in the 1960's, the cartographers will be faced with the biggest job of map making since exploration began.

Now when virgin territory is opened up, it must not only be mapped but its surface features must be named. This task has already been performed for the visible side of the Moon, thanks to the labors of scores of astronomers (mostly amateurs) during the last three centuries. In a way that they could scarcely have imagined, they are about to make a mark on history. For the names they gave to the lunar plains and mountains will soon pass into the vocabulary of mankind, as they blaze forth in the headlines of the future.

It is unfortunate, therefore, that so many of these names are fanciful, cumbersome or downright inappropriate. Since all the major formations on this side of the Moon have already been labeled, it is probably too late to do much about them except in the most extreme cases. (Future lunar colonists may take violent objection to living in Hell, the Marsh of Putridity or the Lake of Death.) The least we can do, however, is to make sure that the maps of the other side are less medieval and inconvenient.

The man who created the pattern of lunar nomenclature we are stuck with today was a Jesuit astronomer, Joannes Riccioli, of Bologna, Italy, who published his map of the Moon in 1651. This was some forty years after Galileo had made his first telescope and astonished the world with the news that the Moon was not, as Aristotle had taught, a perfectly smooth sphere, but was even more mountainous than the Earth.

Father Riccioli's scheme for naming the new world that had been revealed in his lifetime was a consistent one, based on the fact that there are three main types of lunar formation—the dark, almost level plains, the mountain ranges and the craters. The plains are easily visible to the naked eye, and their patterns have given rise to countless myths and legends—such as that of the angry warrior mentioned in *Hiawatha* who:

> Seized his grandmother, and threw her
> Up into the sky at midnight;
> Right against the moon he threw her;
> 'Tis her body that you see there.

In a low-powered telescope, the dark regions look very much like areas of water, and they are also at a considerably lower elevation than the brighter parts of the Moon. Though Riccioli knew perfectly well that they were dry plains, he christened them seas (mare, plural maria), oceans, lakes, bays and so on. In the actual naming he really let his imagination go, being strongly influenced by astrological ideas and the notion that the Moon's first quarter promotes good weather while its last quarter brings storms and rain. Here are some of the more picturesque names which survive to this day on all maps of the Moon: Ocean of Storms (Oceanus

Procellarum); Sea of Tranquillity; Sea of Nectar; Sea of Crises; Sea of Spring (Mare Veris); Sea of Rains (Mare Imbrium); Sea of Clouds (Mare Nubium); Bay of Rainbows (Sinus Iridum); Marsh of Dreams (Palus Somnii). We can be slightly thankful that, somewhere in the last three centuries, Riccioli's Bay of Epidemics and Peninsula of Delirium have dropped by the wayside.

Skirting many of these dark areas are magnificent mountain ranges, some of them as high as the Himalayas, and here Riccioli took the easy way out. Following the suggestion of the astronomer Hevelius, he simply transposed terrestrial names to the Moon. So today we have the lunar Alps, Apennines, Urals, Carpathians and Pyrenees.

The problem of finding names for the Moon's relatively few seas, lakes, bays and mountain ranges is as nothing to that of identifying the innumerable craters. The largest map so far produced—a 300-inch-diameter chart made by the British observer Dr. H. P. Wilkins—shows about 90,000 craters, ranging from walled plains big enough to enclose Vermont or Maryland, down to tiny pits a fraction of a mile across.

Even the first crude telescopes could show at least a thousand craters, but Riccioli did not attempt to name them all. He contented himself with about two hundred, which was quite enough to start with, and the names he chose were those of great astronomers, philosophers or scientists. The precedent thus established has, with very few exceptions, lasted to this day.

It is amusing to note how Father Riccioli's personal prejudices colored his map making. An extraordinarily large number of craters bear the names of fellow Jesuits, but it is only fair to point out that they were mostly men of scientific distinction. (Even today, any large gathering of astronomers will contain a substantial number of Jesuits; the order has practically monopolized certain departments of geophysics.) When Riccioli published his map, the historic debate as to whether the Earth was the center of the Universe, or merely another planet circling the Sun, was still in full swing. Galileo had been haled up before the Inquisition only eighteen years earlier and forced to recant his belief in a moving Earth, and Copernicus' great book, *The Revolution of the Celestial Orbs,* which founded modern astronomy, was still on the *Index Expurgatorius,* where it remained until well into the nineteenth century.

Though Riccioli could hardly ignore Galileo, the most outstanding scientist of his age, he attached his name to a small and insignificant crater tucked away near the western edge of the Moon. The conspicuous craters he reserved for the orthodox, party-line astronomers, with the result that some of the mightiest formations on the Moon are now named after long forgotten philosophers and theologians.

Father Riccioli did, however, make a few concessions which he must have found difficult to reconcile with his conscience. Though as a faithful son of the Church he believed that the Copernican doctrine of the moving Earth was a heresy, his personal admiration for Copernicus was so great that he gave him what is perhaps the most splendid, though not the largest, crater on the face of the Moon. The most conspicuous one of all—easily visible to the naked eye —he gave to Tycho Brahe, the last great astronomer to cling to the outmoded, earth-centered model of the Universe.

In the three centuries since Riccioli, generations of later selenographers have followed his system and given personal names to craters. The result is that the Moon has become, in Descartes' phrase, "a graveyard of astronomers." The term "graveyard" is not altogether accurate, for there are some sixty individuals alive today who have lunar craters named after them. At the last count, thirteen were Americans, the majority of the remained British and Spanish. There are also French, Italian, Japanese, German and Finnish representatives on the Moon, but—curiously enough—not a single living Russian, and only three dead ones. (I suspect that contemporary Soviet moon maps may show a different state of affairs.)

The right to christen a crater goes only to someone who has made a serious contribution to lunar studies, and even then the name has to be approved by the International Astronomical Union to make it official. At the moment slightly more than seven hundred lunar formations have personal names attached to them, and a study of the list is a fascinating occupation which not only produces some surprises but may also give useful hints for the future.

Altogether, more than thirty craters possess American names; the most celebrated is undoubtedly Benjamin Franklin, who owns a small crater (well, small for the Moon, since it's only thirty-four miles across) not far from the Sea of Serenity. And it must be admitted (*Pravda* please copy) that two United States citizens purchased their lunar immortality with hard cash, not with the imponderable currency of scientific knowledge. Yet, considering the services they rendered to astronomy, it is not likely that many will grudge the financiers Lick and Yerkes their place on the Moon.

Let us wander through the directory of lunar craters and stop at interesting or familiar names. The very first one listed is an old friend from English literature—Abenezra, or "Rabbi ben Ezra" of Browning's poem. What's *he* doing on the Moon? Well, he was a distinguished Jewish astronomer of the twelfth century and so has a perfect right to his position.

One cannot really say the same for Alexander the Great, who was put on the Moon merely to keep company with Julius Caesar. Julius, however, has a good claim, having earned it by his reform of the calendar. And while we are on the subject of military men, it is somewhat startling to meet Field Marshal Graf von Moltke owning a tiny crater, rather inappropriately close to the Sea of Tranquillity. Moltke's place on the Moon was given to him (by a German astronomer, needless to say) in recognition of the fact that he persuaded the Prussian government to print an important lunar map. There is no reason to suppose that this was inspired by any early ideas of interplanetary imperialism; Moltke was himself an energetic explorer and map maker who surveyed remote parts of Asia which no European had ever visited.

Famous explorers are well represented on the Moon; among those of the part are Colombo (Columbus), Cook, Marco Polo, Pytheas, Megelhaens (Magellan) and Vasco da Gama. Coming up to more modern times, Nansen, Shackleton, Peary, Amundsen and Scott may be found clustering round the lunar poles.

Scattered across the face of the Moon will be found the names of some of history's supreme intellects. Here is a brief listing: Archimedes, Aristotle, Darwin, Descartes, da Vinci, Einstein, Euclid, Kant, Kepler, Leibnitz, Newton, Plato, Pythagoras. Unfortunately, but inevitably, the later scientists and philosophers have had a raw deal, being fobbed off with very second-rate formations. The sad case of Einstein is a good example; he has been given a sorry little crater less than thirty miles across, so near the edge of the Moon that it is almost impossible to see and might just as well be on the other side.

In contrast, the names attached to many fine craters are so obscure that only devoted historical research can uncover their origins. Others look fairly straightforward, but are quite misleading. The crater Hell, for example, was not named because of any supposed satanic associations; it commemorates Father Maximilian Hell, S.J., once Director of Vienna Observatory. Luther is not Martin, but a much later German—a nineteenth century astronomer. The crater Pallas is not named after the Greek Goddess (who already claims a minor planet) but a German explorer. Beer, disappointingly, turns out to be a Berlin banker celebrated for his astronomical studies but much less well-known to the world at large than his brother, the composer Meyerbeer. And though one of the Americans enshrined on the Moon is Holden, he got there *via* Lick Observatory, not Hollywood. There are as yet no film stars on the Moon, though probably this is only a matter of time.

Many of the people with lunar holdings had highly checkered careers on Earth, and not a few met violent ends. Several (Lavoisier, the great chemist; Condorcet, the philosopher; Bailly, astronomer and mayor of Paris) made their exits with the aid of that highly scientific device, the guillotine. One—Cichus—was burned at the stake for necromancy, in the days when astronomy and astrology were still confused even by the intelligent.

This confusion brought disaster to the tenant of a small crater on the extreme eastern edge of the Moon. Ulug-Beg, grandson of Tamerlane, was a great patron of the sciences, and founded a splendid observatory near his capital, Samarkand. Unfortunately, when he took the natural precaution of casting the horoscope of his eldest son, he was perturbed to find that the boy was destined to kill him.

Unlike most Oriental potentates, who knew how to deal with this standard situation, Ulug-Beg did not beat the young man to the draw but merely exiled him. Needless to say, he returned at the head of an invading army and, like a dutiful son, fulfilled his father's prediction. Thereafter, the historians record with a fine sense of retraint, "astronomy was no longer cultivated in Samarkand."

Another obscure name, near the south pole of the Moon, is associated with my favorite story of scientific hard luck. In the days when a journey to the Far East was a major undertaking, the French astronomer Legentil sailed to India to observe the transit of Venus across the Sun. It took place on June 6, 1761, but Legentil couldn't make the appointment; he had been delayed on the high seas by the current Anglo-French war, and when he arrived at Pondichéry the show was over. However, another transit was due in almost exactly eight years, s the stubborn astronomer decided to sit it out.

And so, in 1769, he was in the right place at the right time—but, *hélas,* the transit was completely obscured by clouds. Legentil couldn't see a thing; this, however, was not the end of his bad luck.

As the next performance was not due for a hundred and five years, he packed his things and sadly sailed for France. And when he got there, he discovered that all his property had been sold, his family having assumed that by this time he must be dead. . . .

That is enough for this side of the Moon; though one could spend a lifetime exploring it—as many have—the other hemisphere is beckoning. Yet before we cross to it, it may be well to mention briefly why there is an "other side" which we have never been able to observe. The facts are simple, but it is astonishing how poorly they are understood. One sign of the popular confusion is the expression "the dark side of the Moon." There is no such place; the Moon turns under the Sun in 29½ days, and each face is equally illuminated during this period. Any darkness is purely temporary, as on Earth; the interchange of night and day is merely more leisurely.

Earth and Moon perform a kind of celestial dance together, and in most dances you cannot see the back of your partner's head. But imagine that the male partner, in addition to performing the dance movement, is also spinning round and round, as in some of the more energetic ballets. You then have an accurate analogy of the present Earth-Moon situation. The female partner—the Moon—sees each side of the male partner—Earth. But Earth sees only the face of the Moon, not the back of her head.

You will not be surprised to hear that this is a temporary

state of affairs, and that the Earth will be unable to keep it up forever. The performance is too exhausting, and in a few billion years the dance will have settled down to a sedate and stately waltz, each partner content to stare perpetually into the other's face. When that time comes, one side of the Earth will never see the Moon, as today one side of the Moon never sees the Earth.

There is not the slightest reason to suppose that the Moon's hidden side differs in any way from the one we can see. In fact, we can observe a small portion of it, because the Moon rocks slightly on her axis during the course of her revolution round the Earth, and this enables us to peer a little way over the edge. This border region is so badly foreshortened that it cannot be accurately mapped, but because of its existence we can see about 60 per cent of the Moon, not merely 50 per cent.

We must assume that, as soon as we can observe the far side of the Moon, we will be confronted with some scores of mountain ranges and "seas," and at least a hundred thousand craters—all totally anonymous, all waiting to be named.

As far as the still-to-be-discovered mountain ranges are concerned, there is no problem. Earth's greatest peaks were unknown when the Moon was first mapped; there are no lunar Himalayas, Rockies or Andes. These evocative names are crying out for mountains to match them, and we can be sure that they will be forthcoming. Also available as lunar candidates are the Appalachians, the Sierras, the Pamirs and dozens of individual peaks such as Everest, Kilimanjaro, Whitney, Popocatepetl, Kanchenjunga, Nanda Devi. . . .

The new plains—the dusky, and possibly dusty, lunar lowlands—pose some difficulties. Shall we continue to name them after bodies of water? There seems no harm in continuing the custom; it is not likely that anyone will ever be misled by it and pack skin-diving equipment on a trip to the Moon. But if the practice is continued, then the astrological and occult associations will certainly be discarded, though we need not abandon the poetic touch which gives such charm to so many lunar place names. It may be simplest to transpose terrestrial lakes and seas; the supply is certainly adequate, and when we consider how the Moon controls the tides, the idea of loaning it our oceans seems highly appropriate.

It is when we come to the craters that matters start getting complicated. Finding a hundred thousand names in a hurry would be no easy task, though luckily the problem is not quite so bad as that. Once a few hundred major formations have been named, the smaller ones can be referred to—as postal districts are in a large city—by adding letters or numbers as suffixes. This has long been standard procedure for the visible face of the Moon; thus a small crater inside the ninety-mile-diameter walled plain of Ptolemaeus might be referred to as Ptolemaeus B, or Ptolemaeus 123. (In this single case, incidentally, there are over three hundred sub-craters!)

Through sheer inertia, if for no other reason, we will probably continue to give the lunar craters personal names. But whose names? The practice of honoring great scientists and philosophers is obviously worth continuing, and we might start by redressing some of the present injustices. Galileo, Newton and Einstein should be relocated in the most splendid of the far-side craters, and their current substandard residences handed over to less important people. And Maxwell, Hertz, Roentgen, Becquerel, Curie, Rutherford, Planck and the other makers of modern science should also be suitably rewarded.

The men who paved the way to the actual conquest of space—the great pioneers of astronautics, such as Tsiolkovsky, Oberth and Goddard—most certainly deserve conspicuous lunar landmarks, and though there have so far been no nonhuman names on the Moon, surely a modest crater can be dedicated to Laika, the first space traveler.

It would not be difficult to find sufficient scientists, living or dead, to label the major features on both sides of the Moon. However, now that the matter is no longer of interest only to a handful of specialists, there will be claims from other quarters. Some of these will be well grounded; it is a slight scandal that there are no artists, composers or poets on the Moon, despite all the attention they have paid to our satellite. (One exception: Leonardo has a small crater in the Moon's western—i.e. first—quadrant, but he is there because of his scientific interests, not his artistic attainments. And though there is a Wagner tucked away in the Carpathian Mountains, he turns out to be a nineteenth-century German —physiologist!) Surely Dante, Homer, Michelangelo, Bach,

Shakespeare, Milton, Goethe, Beethoven, to mention only the first who come to mind, will not be blacklisted if their names are proposed.

A slightly more controversial suggestion would be the names of the great religious leaders and reformers who have shaped the thoughts and lives not of mere millions, but of billions. Moses, Akhenaton, Asoka, Mohammed, Lao-tse, Confucius and Gautama certainly merit apotheosis. The last three would probably have reached the Moon centuries ago, had it not been for the unexplained omission of the Chinese to invent the telescope.

The real trouble will start when the politicians and statesmen try to climb aboard the lunar bandwagon. The few already there got in by the back door; and are in any event sufficiently remote not to arouse prejudices: No one today objects violently to Alexander or Casear, and there would probably be few protests against the nominations of Washington, Napoleon or Lincoln. But as we approach our own time, universal agreement would become more difficult. Though millions would approve of Lenin, Roosevelt or Churchill, millions more would take a dim view of granting them lunar franchises.

The obvious solution is to allow no one on the Moon until he has been dead for a safe period—say fifty years. That is long enough, in most cas⟨s⟩, for greatness to be established, and for contemporary passions to evaporate. It would also eliminate the celebrities whose fame looms large in their own generation, but are unknown to posterity.

If this rule is followed, then the Moon can indeed become a Roll of Honor for all mankind. Let us hope that the cartographers and photo-reconnaissance experts who must now undertake the task of naming a world do so in the spirit of responsibility and dignity it demands. We do not want to wake up one morning, to find that the job has been done in top secrecy by a Pentagon general who happens to be a baseball fan, or an unimaginative bureaucrat who has stuck pins at random into the Vladivostok telephone directory.

For the names we are about to write upon those unknown plains and peaks and craters will be more than chapter headings in the history of the future. They will be the words many of our grandchildren will utter, when they speak of home.

★ THE RADIO UNIVERSE
★

★ For thousands of years men have looked up at the Sun, Moon and stars—and believed that they saw the Universe. Within the last decade, we have discovered that they saw only *one* Universe, and that another exists, invisible to the eye. This is the Universe revealed not by light, but by the millionfold longer waves of radio. It has been a revelation indeed; today's astronomers are like blind men who have suddenly been granted the gift of sight. It will be years before they can fully interpret what they see—or, rather, what their wonderful new instrument, the radiotelescope, sees for them.

The discovery of radio waves themselves is still less than a century old; it was as recently as 1873 that the great physicist James Clerk-Maxwell predicted their existence theoretically, and not until 1888 that Hertz first generated them in the laboratory. The swift rise of radio communication in the 1900's is one of the romances of modern technology, but for a long time it never occurred to scientists that Nature, as well as Man, could produce radio waves. It was true that brief bursts of "static" or interference accompanied lightning flashes—as everyone knows who has ever listened to a radio program during a thunderstorm—but this was not considered to be of very great scientific importance, though it gave the meteorologists a useful tool for tracking distant storms.

The first man to suspect that we might be missing something was a Bell Telephone Laboratories engineer named Karl Jansky, who was trying to hunt down the source of the background noise which can be heard in any radio receiver when the volume is turned full up. Some of this familiar hissing or frying sound originates in the set itself, but part of it is picked up by the antenna. In 1931 Jansky made the surprising discovery that part of this radio noise came from outer space, from the general direction of the Milky Way.

This discovery would have earned Jansky a Nobel Prize if anyone had appreciated its significance at the time; but— like some of the results of psychical research—it could not be fitted into the general pattern of accepted science. So, for almost fifteen years, it was virtually forgotten.

It took the radar developments of the Second World War to bring the facts of radio-astronomy so forcibly to the attention of scientists that they could no longer be overlooked. Early in 1942 the British army's anti-aircraft radar was suddenly and inexplicably jammed by a new type of interference. Naturally, the Germans got the blame, but it did not take long to discover that the trouble was a good deal further away. The "jamming" was coming from the Sun.

At the time, this was a well-kept secret, but immediately after the war the scientists concerned—mostly British and Australian—started following up this new line of investigation with great energy. They were much helped by the fact that large quantities of surplus radar equipment could be picked up for a song, and most of the first radio-astronomy equipment was built round converted radar sets. It is, however, important to distinguish between the two techniques, similar though they are. In radar proper, a pulse of radio energy is sent out into space and the returning echo is received a fraction of a second later. In this way, it is possible to range the Moon and to detect meteors invisible by any other means. Most of radio-astronomy, however, is concerned with detecting radio waves produced by distant natural sources, not echoing back from man-made transmitters.

These natural sources fall into several very different categories, and there are certainly many others still to be discovered. One of them, as the British army's radar experts found to their discomfort, is the Sun. However, the greater part of the time the Sun is not a very powerful source of radio waves; if you listen to it on a sensitive receiver you will usually hear only a gentle sizzling. But occasionally, when the enormous dark blemishes known as sunspots cross the solar disk, the output of radio waves increases by many millionfold. Other potent sources of radio emisions are flares —sudden eruptions of incandescent gas from the Sun's surface, on a scale which makes our most violent H-bomb explosion about as impressive as the popping of a paper bag.

Precisely how these torrents and whirlpools of flaming gas, at temperatures of thousands of degrees, and moving at hundreds of miles a second, act as generators of radio waves is still being investigated by scientists. Their work will lead to a much better understanding of the Sun, and it is also linked with research which before long may transform life here on Earth. For the study of such electrified gases is an essential step on the road to thermonuclear power—the release of the sea's infinite energy for the use of all mankind. The Sun started fusing hydrogen several billion years ago; now we are learning from its example.

That the Sun was a source of radio waves did not surprise the astronomers greatly, though they were rather taken aback by the strength of its most violent transmissions. What no one could have foreseen, however, was that radio waves would also be received from far colder bodies, such as the planets Venus and Jupiter.

In the case of Venus, Earth's perpetually cloud-covered twin, the intermittent radio disturbances may come from something analogous to thunderstorms. Being nearer the Sun, Venus is a good deal hotter than Earth and its weather must be—to put it mildly—tropical. In any event, the bursts of radio noise emerging from beneath the eternal clouds may give us our first definite information concerning conditions on the hidden surface of the planet.

The case of Jupiter is much more mysterious. This giant planet, ten times the diameter of Earth, is a hundred degrees colder than the most frigid Antarctic night—so cold, indeed, that most ordinary gases are liquefied. Yet from somewhere deep down in the turbulent, half-frozen slush of methane, ammonia and hydrogen, through which move floating islands bigger than our planet, are radio sources of immense power, generating millions of times more energy than terrestrial thunderstorms.

Very feeble radio waves have also been detected from the Moon and Mars. These, however, are merely the waves that are produced by any object not at the absolute zero of temperature, simply through the heat vibrations of its molecules. The radio waves which come from Jupiter and the Sun are vastly more powerful than can be explained by this "thermal" effect, and must have a completely different origin.

But the greatest of all radio transmitters in the Universe are far more remote than Sun and planets, and their investigation leads us back to Jansky's original discovery. If our eyes could see radio waves as they now see light waves, most of the sky would appear covered with a faintly glowing mist. The glow would concentrate into a bright band closely matching the position of the Milky Way, but scattered over the heavens would also be hundreds of individual points of radio "light," some of them extremely brilliant. These were originally, and rather naturally, given the name "radio stars" —but it was soon found that most of them did not coincide with any outstanding visible stars. The astronomers were suddenly confronted with an entirely new picture of the sky, and the attempt to find the origin of the radio stars (or discrete sources, as they are now more noncommittally called) has been one of the most fascinating scientific detective stories of the past decade.

Some of these radio sources—millions of millons of millions of times more powerful than any transmitters built by Man—are filaments of heated gas, expanding and twisting through space with great velocity. They may be the debris of exploding stars; indeed, this is known to be the case for one of the most powerful radio sources (the Crab Nebula—remnant of a cosmic catastrophe which the Chinese astronomers observed as a brilliant but short-lived new star in A.D. 1054).

These swirling gas clouds, calling attention to their existence by the roar of their radio voices, are merely local eddies in that whirlpool of stars, the Galaxy. Though they are far larger than the Solar System, being many light-years across, they are still very small on the cosmic scale. And as radio transmitters, they cannot be compared with the most stupendous source of radio energy yet discovered.

This lies in the heart of the constellation Cygnus, but it is a million times further away than the cross-shaped group of stars which outlines the figure of the flying swan. It is pouring out radio waves at the unimaginable rate of 1,000,000-000,000,000,000,000,000,000 megawatts; for comparison, a high-powered radio station may broadcast *one* megawatt. When this intense source was discovered, barely ten years ago, the astronomers were baffled because the best telescopes could find nothing visible to account for it. Eventually, photographs taken at Mount Palomar by Baade and Minkowski revealed a tiny smudge of light which has now been interpreted as one of the most awe-inspiring phenomena yet discovered. It is nothing less than the head-on collision of two galaxies.

This is indeed a phrase worth savoring with the mind, but the word "collision" is a little misleading. It will take millions of years for the two great systems of stars to sweep through each other, and it is most unlikely that even a single pair of stars will actually come into contact, so vast are the distances between them. It is the violent interaction between the tenuous gas clouds *between* the stars which generates this tremendous pulse of power. Even from 270,000,000 light-years away, it dominates the radio sky; our present crude instruments could detect it at a far greater range than the two-hundred-inch telescope can observe.

Conditions must be very peculiar in a region so drenched with radiation as the Cygnus radio source. One could probably draw sparks off any piece of bare metal, and radio communication would be as impossible as a quiet conversation in a jet-engine test cell. It is difficult to see how the inhabitants of any planets in these colliding galaxies could even discover the laws of electromagnetism, in the presence of such a roaring background of power.

And this leads us naturally to a question which many people would like to ask, but which the astronomers are chary of answering. Is there any evidence at all of signals due to intelligence among the barrage of radio noise pouring down from space?

Not yet; nor could it reasonably be expected in the present early stage of this new science. The natural radio transmitters scattered round the sky are quadrillions of times more powerful than any that even the most advanced civilizations could possibly build; against the cosmic cacophony, the voice of intelligence could be only the faintest of whispers. Our own radio signals now fill an expanding sphere of space more than a hundred light-years across; Marconi's first transmissions are already fifteen times further away than the nearest star. But long before they left the Solar System, our most powerful broadcasts will have faded so far below the background of interstellar noise that they are as undetectable as words that were spoken yesterday. No receiver, however sensitive, can pick up signals once they have sunk below the noise level. And if we ever do detect intelligent signals from space, the beings that produced them may no longer exist—such is the slowness of radio waves, compared with the immensity of the Universe. That soundless thunderclap from the colliding galaxies in Cygnus started on its way before the great reptiles trampled the Earth.

Yet, though they may deny it with some indignation, many radio astronomers must cherish the secret hope that some day they will detect signals which do not have a natural origin. The telescopes already built—such as the 250-foot-diameter giant at Jodrell Bank, Manchester, famous for its Sputnik and moon-rocket tracking—are the products of the very first decade of radio-astronomy. One day they will be superseded by far larger instruments, possibly miles across.

These will not be built on the Earth's surface, but will be assembled in satellite orbits, where the absence of gravity will permit the use of paper-thin materials and ultralight construction techniques. Clear of the man-made interference which now drenches our planet, they will be able to gather far more energy than today's antenna systems and, what is equally important, will be able to focus with much greater precision upon selected small regions of space. We can be certain that these vast instruments will bring us much nearer to a true understanding of our Universe; and we can hope that, one day, they will tell us that we are not alone in its immensity.

★ OF SPACE AND THE SPIRIT
★

★ ASTRONOMY is the oldest of the sciences, and the one which has not only the widest popular appeal but also the most profound philosophical implications. This was never more true than at the present time, when the horizons of human knowledge are not so much exanding as exploding. New discoveries and techniques—such as the development of electronic instruments, the launching of artificial satellites, the detection of radio waves from space—have invigorated the whole science and shed new light on problems over which men have argued in vain for centuries.

Yet what has already happened is merely the prelude to far more startling events. In a period which will be very short by the standards of history—perhaps a century at the most—we may have established physical contact with all the major solid bodies in the Solar System. A landing on the remotest of the Sun's planets may now be nearer to us in time than the Battle of Gettysburg.

The shadow of these coming events already lies across our age, stirring the thoughts of all men who have ever stared at the night sky and wondered what part our race is destined to play in the unfolding drama of the Universe. Many of the great questions of religion and philosophy must now be re-formulated, and there is more than a possibility that some which seemed forever beyond hope of solution may soon be answered.

Whether intelligent life exists outside the Earth is, per-haps, unique among these problems in its intellectual and emotional appeal. The only type of life which we can im-agine without losing ourselves in biological fantasies must be planet-based, and until a short time ago astronomers felt re-luctantly certain that planets were exceedingly rare phe-nomena. Indeed, they were regarded as the results of cosmic accidents that could occur only a very few times in the entire history of any well-conducted universe.

Today we are fairly confident that the exact reverse is true; modern theories of the formation of the Solar System suggest that many, if not most, stars must have planets re-volving around them. This outlook was given considerable support by the detection, in 1942, of a hitherto unknown body—much too small to be a Sun—in the double-star sys-tem 61 Cygni. This binary star is one of our closest neigh-bors; it would be a most remarkable coincidence, if planets were indeed rare, to find a specimen practically on our door-steps. If we eliminate systems which, through the instability of the central sun or for some other reason, seem unpromising as the abodes of life, we may not be far from the truth if we guess that one star in ten possesses at least one planet upon which life could theoretically exist.

This leads us to the second and equally remarkable transformation which the last ten or fifteen years has brought. As recently as 1947 it was possible for du Noüy, in his widely read book *Human Destiny*, to maintain that living things could not possibly arise from "dead" inorganic matter by the operation of purely natural forces. The complexity of even the simplest single-celled organism was so enormous that to expect atoms of carbon, hydrogen, oxygen and the rest to form it by spontaneous aggregation was much less probable than that Eddington's famous army of simian typists should produce the entire works of Shakespeare at the first attempt. Life's appearance on Earth (or elsewhere) must therefore have been consciously directed and controlled by some organizing force, which it was tempting to identify as the hand of God.

We now know, thanks to the work of such biologists as Bernal and Oparin, that this apparently convincing argument is wholly fallacious, and that life can probably evolve from nonliving matter in the circumstances that must exist upon many primitive, newly formed planets. The process may, indeed, be inevitable when we are dealing with astronomical time periods; the idea that life on this planet is some kind of freak or special creation has vanished with the belief in the uniqueness of the Solar System. Stanley Miller's famous experiment at the University of Chicago in 1952, when a complex organic soup was produced by the action of electrical discharges upon simple solutions of carbon dioxide, ammonia, methane and other gases, suggests how the first steps in the evolution of life may have taken place. (For an entertaining and not-too-technical account of the way in which the chemicals of life may build themselves up from elementary substances, see the essay "The Unblind Workings of Chance" in Dr. Isaac Asimov's book *Only a Trillion*.)

That both planets and living creatures are common throughout the Universe must, therefore, now be taken as highly probable, though it cannot yet be proved beyond doubt. We may be hopelessly conservative if we guess that life may be associated with one star in every hundred. Dr.

Harlow Shapley, in his book *Of Stars and Men*, reduces the figure to one in a trillion by being deliberately ultrapessimistic; he considers a more reasonable estimate to be one in a million. But any figure is, at the present stage of our semi-ignorance, pure guesswork; let us for the sake of argument settle on that one in a hundred, and see where it leads us.

It implies the existence of a billion life-bearing worlds in our single Galaxy—the whirlpool of stars of which our Sun is an undistinguished out-of-town member, lying in one of the remoter spiral arms. And within the range of our telescopes there are approximately a billion other galaxies.

Now a billion is a number all too familiar in today's budgets and military estimates, but this does not mean that anyone can visualize it. Should you feel like trying, I recommend this simple and highly instructive experiment.

Go down to the nearest beach and collect a bucketful of sand; then bring it home and empty it on the table. You now have in front of you—assuming that the sand is of reasonable fineness—something like a billion separate particles. Sift them through your fingers; each is a distinct entity, different from all its companions. How long would it take you to examine every clearly visible individual in the quite small pile before you? Devoting one minute to each, and working eight hours a day, it would keep you busy for almost six thousand years—the whole span of human history.

That is what a billion means; and now try to imagine that every one of those grains of sand is itself a world, perhaps teeming with life, and perhaps bearing rational creatures who measure their history not in thousands but in millions of years. If you succeed, you have a faint mental picture of our Galaxy; if you wish to visualize the whole observed Universe, however, the operation must be repeated with each grain of sand now representing an entire galaxy.

There is a temptation, when brainwashed by such numbers, to argue that these astronomical vistas are of no practical importance, since we can never have direct knowledge of more than a small—indeed, relatively submicroscopic—portion of the Universe. A similar policy was adopted by those followers of Aristotle who refused to look through Galileo's telescope and to see for themselves that Jupiter, as well as Earth, had moons revolving round it. If they could not be seen by the naked eye, these gentlemen argued, the heretical satellites did not really exist.

However, we cannot pretend that the Universe isn't there, for our own children will be starting to explore it, and even their first modest voyages will completely transform our view of the cosmos. Once we can climb the mere hundred miles or so which separate us from space, and thus establish satellite observatories beyond the murk and haze of the atmosphere, it will be like emerging from a fog into the light of day. *Without traveling any further from Earth than Washington is from New York*, we will have broken through the vision barrier and will be able to view Mars, for example, from an apparent distance of only a few thousand miles. With the telescopes which we will be able to construct and operate under the perfect seeing conditions in space, we may even be able to look for the planets of others suns.

It is obviously impossible to anticipate the discoveries which will be made when we succeed in escaping from Earth; indeed, one characteristic of most really important discoveries is their unexpectedness. At the moment the astronomical evidence suggests that we will find some sort of life in the Solar System (on Mars, almost certainly; on Venus, just possibly) but that we will not encounter intelligence. It would be rather too much to hope that two intelligent races should exist in the same small region of space and at the same moment of time.

The discovery of any form of life, however humble, on the planets would greatly affect our outlook upon the Universe by changing what is now a surmise into a certainty. Even a few lichens on Mars, or a few amoebae in the (still hypothetical) seas of Venus would prove that life is not a rare disease that happens to have attacked the planet Earth. And with that settled, it would be illogical to deny the existence of higher forms elsewhere.

It is just possible that we may find direct proof of this on Mars; even if we have missed the Martians by a few million years, their records will still be written in the rocks of an arid world which knows none of the erosion or the interchange of land and sea which has obliterated so much of our own planet's remote past. But all this is pure, unfounded speculation; until we have reason to believe the contrary, it would be safest to assume that H. sapiens is the only intelligent creature yet to have evolved in the Solar System. To find our equals or our peers, we must go further afield to the planets of other suns.

This, to put it mildly, presents problems. Though we are now about to challenge interplanetary distances, the gulfs separating us from the stars are a million times greater, and light itself takes years to span them. Nevertheless, there are good reasons for thinking that interstellar travel will ultimately be possible. When we have developed really efficient nuclear-propulsion devices, speeds comparable to that of light should be attainable, and round trips to the nearest stars would take about ten years. Though tedious, this would not be out of the question even for manned vessels; such techniques as suspended animation, or the use of purely automatic exploring vessels, would extend this range indefinitely.

Nor need *physical* transportation be necessary. With to-day's electronic techniques stretched to the utmost, we could just about get a readable Morse signal to the nearest star. It might therefore be worth while, as soon as we can establish satellite listening posts well away from the radio racket and electrical interference of Earth, to begin a search for intelligently modulated signals from space. If we can tackle interstellar communication only sixty years after we have invented radio, it is not unreasonable to assume that there may be transmitters within a few light-years of us far more powerful than any we have yet built. Even today, many of our radars must far outrange the Solar System—though we can be thankful that all our commercial radio programs will have faded far below the level of cosmic noise before they can affront any stellar neighbors.

By one means or another, therefore, we may hope to establish the existence of extraterrestrial intelligences before many more decades—or at most centuries—have passed. If anyone still feels doubtful of this, I would remind him of the unfortunate error of Auguste Compte, who rashly proclaimed our eternal ignorance concerning the composition of the stars. The speed and thoroughness with which the spectroscope refuted him is a good reminder that there are no apparently fundamental limits to knowledge which may not be transcended by new techniques or inventions.

Keeping this in mind, it is not premature, and it is certainly stimulating, to consider what effect these undoubted but still unknown revelations will have upon the minds of men. They will certainly accelerate a process which has been gaining momentum since Copernicus dethroned the Earth from the center of creation and started it upon its still-continuing journey to the periphery of the Universe. Today, it is difficult for us to believe that as recently as the time of Shakespeare no one knew that other worlds existed; though the Greek had surmised it, there was no direct proof until the invention of the telescope *circa* 1608, and so to almost all educated men up to a dozen generations ago, our planet *was* the Universe. One might even say that this was still true, for 90 per cent of the human race, until the morning of October 4, 1957.

The expansion of the time scale has had equally striking effects on human thought. Until well into the last century much of the Western world believed in the literal truth of Archbishop Ussher's date for Genesis—4004 B.C.—which may still be found printed in some Bibles. It is indeed curious that so many devout men, during the three hundred years between Galileo and Darwin, stubbornly refused to recognize the grandeur of the Universe in space and time— almost as if determined to disparage the power of God. The Eastern religions avoided this mistake, which has done so much to weaken the prestige of Christianity; the Hindus, for example, take it for granted that the world's history stretches back through aeons of time that quite dwarf the few billions demanded by the astronomers.

As mankind's modest place in the scheme of the Universe is more and more widely recognized—on the emotional as well as the intellectual level—the effects on our racial pride will certainly be profound. To the Psalmist's question, "What is Man, that Thou art mindful of him?" the future may well give the ironic answer, "What, indeed?" Our species has come into existence in the last five-thousandth of the Earth's history, and the entire span of human civilization extends for barely a millionth of that time. Unless we exhibit a conceit which can be aptly termed astronomical, we must assume that there are many, many races in the Universe far more advanced than ours intellectually as well as spiritually. Indeed, the extreme youth of Homo sapiens on any cosmic time scale makes it likely that the vast majority of rational extraterrestrial creatures must be superior to us by millions of years of development.

This prospect has been viewed with some alarm by many Christians, who find it hard to reconcile the existence of other intelligent races with the doctrines of Incarnation and Redemption. If God made Man in His own image, what of all the other creatures who must be made in different images, if they are to survive on alien worlds? And if Christ has saved us alone, what have *we* done to merit such special treatment?

During the last few years these problems—which once seemed quite as abstract as the classic question of the number of angels who could dance on a pin—have engaged several theologians. In his book *Existence and the Christ,* Professor Paul Tillich points out that the Incarnation preached by Christianity is for mankind only, and that other races may have other incarnations. (An idea expressed many years ago by Alice Meynell in her poem "Christ in the Universe":

> . . . in the eternities
> Doubtless we shall compare together, hear
> A million alien Gospels, in what guise
> He trod the Pleiades, the Lyre, the Bear.)

Tillich goes on to conclude: "The manifestation of saving power in one place implies that saving power is operating in all places. The expectation of the Messiah as the bearer of the New Being presupposes that God loves the universe, even though in the appearance of the Christ he actualises this love for historical man alone."

Undoubtedly the most stimulating writer on these matters is C. S. Lewis, professor of literature at Magdalene College, Cambridge University. In two famous novels, *Out of the Silent Planet* and *Voyage to Venus (Perelandra)*, Lewis has developed the theme that only humanity has fallen, and that the creatures on other planets are free from the guilt which requires our redemption. This view of mankind's peculiar depravity, well justified by a glance at the daily papers, implies that our planet is under quarantine; in a recent issue of the *Christian Herald* (April, 1958) Professor Lewis makes it clear that he regards with some disfavor our current attempts to evade this quarantine. "Let us," he remarks, "thank God that we are still very far from travel to other worlds." Unless one considers twenty-five years a very long time, this statement must now be modified to read "travel to other worlds *inhabited by intelligent beings.*"

Another possibility, but one so flattering to our racial pride that it is hard to believe it can be true, is that the redemption of other races will proceed through us—that we, in fact, may one day take salvation to the stars. Remembering how "gun and gospel" have been combined in the past, and the manner in which so many missionaries have attempted to "civilize the natives," Lewis is not at all happy about this prospect. "Would our missionaries," he asks, "recognise an unfallen race if they met it? Would they continue to press upon creatures that did not need to be saved that plan of Salvation which God has appointed for Man? Would they denounce as sins mere differences of behavior which the spiritual and biogolical history of these strange creatures fully justified?"

Anyone who has read accounts of past mission activities (Bradford Smith's *Yankees in Paradise* is an excellent example) will appreciate the force of these questions, and Lewis argues nobly: "We must stand firm against all exploitation and all theological imperialism. . . . Our loyalty is due not to our species but to God. Those who are, or can become, His sons, are our real brothers even if they have shells or tusks. It is spiritual, not biological, kinship that counts." In applauding these sentiments, one can also wish that they were better applied on Earth.

The Catholic Church has already accepted and welcomed the coming of the space age. (Perhaps the outstanding role that Jesuit scientists have played in astrophysics has something to do with this.) In 1956, the International Astronautical Federation held a congress in Rome and heard a lengthy and learned address from Pope Pius XII in which he expressed the view that now that Man has discovered the means of exploring the Universe, God clearly intends him to use it. This is a ruling which most men, whatever their beliefs, will surely accept. Any path to knowledge is a path to God—or to Reality, whichever word one prefers to use.

We may conclude, therefore, that any fears that space exploration will shatter the bases of existing religions are unfounded. Nevertheless, the tremendous flood of new knowledge which will accrue from space travel (and which indeed is already flowing down from today's satellites) will in due course profoundly modify our philosophical and religious beliefs. Anyone who doubts this need only glance at the overwhelming impact of science upon faith during the past few centuries; the now settled controversies over the Earth's movement round the Sun and the evolution of Man are the classic examples. Even in the last hundred years, many beliefs passionately held by the leaders of the great religions have ceased to be accepted by their equally devout successors. It would be absurd to imagine that this process will come to an end, just at the moment when science is about to make the greatest breakthrough in all history.

At this moment in time, at the very beginning of the centuries-long gold rush into ever richer, ever expanding fields of knowledge, we must realize that there is no hope of understanding our Universe until we have examined a fairly large sample of it—certainly a good deal more than one small planet out of billions. Though this cautious attitude may disappoint many who are hot for certainties, any other policy would be utterly naïve. It would put us in the same position as Pacific islanders who have never yet had any contact with the world beyond their coral reef, yet who attempt to construct a picture of the whole Earth and its peoples from the view they get from the top of their highest palm tree.

Harlow Shapley, in the already-mentioned *Of Stars and Men*, looks forward to our present "anthropomorphic religions and philosophies, which have so often been conspicuously earth-bound and much tangled up with the human mind and human behavior" expanding to embrace these new revelations of science, adding that "a one-planet deity has for me little appeal." The British astronomer Fred Hoyle, in the controversial series of radio talks which became the well-known book *The Nature of the Universe*, took an uncompromisingly materialist view which caused much heart-burning and ink-slinging among his listeners. He concluded that there is no evidence for the existence of God in the Universe around us, religion presumably being an illusion of the human mind.

On this view, it must be assumed that when we contact superior extraterrestrial intelligences we shall find that belief in a supernatural order of things marks an early stage of development amongst most rational creatures, and perishes with the rise of science. Most disconcerting of all would be the discovery that Man alone is a myth-making animal, forever impelled to fill the gaps in his knowledge by fantasies. (Yet if this be the price we have had to pay for the whole realm of art, which is always an attempt to create the nonexistent, we need not be ashamed. We will be better off than beings who posses all knowledge, but know nothing of poetry and music.)

Whatever the outcome of our discoveries and adventures in space, the fact will remain that the real Universe is more miraculous than any miracle. And even if every man now alive, seen from a century hence, appears no more than "a savage suckled in an outworn creed," that will leave God precisely where He has always been, if He is anywhere—back at the beginning of creation, X billion years ago. (As of today, $X = 5$. But remember Archbishop Ussher.) Perhaps when God reached zero of the cosmic countdown, He turned His attention elsewhere, knowing that His work with us was done. It will certainly not diminish His glory—rather the reverse—if we discover that, in all the ages since time began, He has never tinkered with the mechanism of the Universe. Only an unskilled craftsman is forced to make perpetual adjustments to his handiwork; the real expert packs his tools and walks away when the job is done. . . .

Let us, therefore, wait in a spirit of expectant humility for whatever light the future may throw upon these great questions, remembering that our intellectual sincerity may well be judged by our lack of apprehension. No honest man was ever afraid of the truth.

Faiths come and go, but Truth abides. Out there among the stars lie such truths as we may understand, whether we learn them by our own efforts, or from the strange teachers who are waiting for us along the infinite road on which our feet are now irrevocably set.

Envoi

Across the gulf of centuries, the blind smile of Homer is turned upon our age. Along the echoing corridors of time, the roar of the rockets merges now with the creak of the wind-taut rigging. For somewhere in the world today, still unconscious of his destiny, walks the boy who will be the first Odysseus of the Age of Space. . . .

ARTHUR C. CLARKE

I was born at Minehead, in the West of England, in 1917, and such ancestors as I can trace all appear to have been farmers. My interest in science began early, and I can pinpoint the actual event which stimulated it. When I was less than ten years old my father gave me a cigarette card from a series depicting prehistoric animals, and at once I became fascinated by paleontology. For a while I avidly collected fossils; however, I soon switched to astronomy, building small telescopes from cardboard tubes and lenses, and spending my nights mapping the Moon. Before long I knew the lunar landscape much better than my native Somerset.

Throughout my teens, while my widowed mother was struggling to make a living from our small farm, I spent my time building scientific gadgets. The most ambitious was a photophone transmitter made from a bicycle lamp, which could send speech for several yards along a light-beam. I also attempted the audio-modulation of sunlight by purely mechanical means and a device based on this principle has now been developed for space communications.

The science-fiction virus attacked me when I was fourteen and saw my first copies of *Amazing* and *Astounding* Stories. At once my life was transformed, and for years I collected every science-fiction magazine I could lay my hands upon. I can still recall the thrill of receiving an entire crateful of *Wonder Stories* which I'd purchased for five cents apiece, and feel sorry for modern youngsters who are surfeited by the current glut of science-fiction. Back in the 30's every book and magazine was a collector's item.

At fifteen, I started writing short pieces for the school magazine, and eventually became its assistant editor. At nineteen I passed the Civil Service Executive examination and moved to London, where I encountered the British science-fiction world (about ten of us, including John Wyndham, Eric Frank Russell, William F. Temple, John Carnell, and Walter Gillings) and the embryo British Interplanetary Society. Before long I became treasurer of the B.I.S.—its annual income was then about £100—edited, wrote for and duplicated countless science-fiction 'fan-mags', and sold my first articles on space-flight. For the record, the very first money I ever made from writing came from Eric Frank Russell, who generously shared the proceeds of a story to which I had contributed a few ideas. The first articles I sold in my own right were to Walter Gillings' pioneer science-fiction magazine, *Tales of Wonder*, in 1938.

The War and the R.A.F. jolted me out of the Civil Service and introduced me to radar. The experience I gained working with the prototype Ground Controlled Approach system has been reflected in many of my stories and one novel, and it also introduced me at first hand to the scientific mind. During this period I had the most important idea of my life, and incorporated it in a paper, *Extraterrestrial Relays*, which was published in the October 1945 issue of *Wireless World*. This was the first proposal for the use of satellites for radio and T.V. communication; in particular I stressed the value of the 24-hour orbit. Had I realised how quickly this idea would materialise, I would certainly have attempted to patent it—though it is some slight consolation to know that an application would probably have failed in 1945.

My service career was a very peaceful one; those who had to rough it will be interested to know that I fought the latter half of the war accompanied by a 3-inch astronomical refractor, a Remington Noiseless Portable and a fair-sized library. I sold my first stories to the American science-fiction market while still in the R.A.F. and continued to do so through college. (*Prelude To Space* was written during my first summer vacation.) After graduation from King's College, London, with a B.Sc. in physics and maths, I became Assistant Editor of *Physics Abstracts*. This extremely interesting job kept me in contact with the whole field of current research, but after two years I discovered that my spare-time income was exceeding my salary. Even before the Book-of-the-Month Club selected my second work of nonfiction, *The Exploration of Space*, I had decided to free-lance.

Much of my spare time in the 1945-55 period was taken

up with the rapidly-expanding British Interplanetary Society, of which I have twice been Chairman. I was also Chairman of the International Astronautical Federation Congress in London (1951) and of the Hayden Planetarium Symposium on Spaceflight (New York, 1953).

In the mid-50's, however, my career took a new direction when I was badly bitten by the skin-diving virus. (I have since infected other astronauts, notably Dr. Wernher von Braun.) In 1955 I joined my partner Mike Wilson on the Great Barrier Reef of Australia, with results reported in *The Coast of Coral*. Later expeditions took us to Ceylon, where we have now made our home and which has provided material for several books. These submarine excursions were interrupted by U.S. lecture tours in 1957-59, which I found very enjoyable and stimulating—but the lure of the tropics has proved too strong for me to resume them.

At the moment my score stands at 30 books and some 200 articles or short stories in *Holiday, Playboy, Horizon, Reader's Digest* and most of the science-fiction magazines. Probably the short story is my favourite medium, but I would hate to be restricted either to fiction or nonfiction, to sea or to space.

As I am now in the disconcerting position of seeing all the things I wrote about in my twenties and thirties coming true (to a degree beyond my wildest expectations) in my forties, I feel rather like an unemployed prophet. But this does not worry me unduly, for I have so many interests that I will never have to look far for literary stimulus.

Indeed, at the moment I have only to look three yards, for in front of me as I type these words is a wooden chest containing the highly unexpected by-products of our last underwater expedition. Mike went to make a film . . . and came back with two beautiful little bronze cannon, and more than a hundredweight of pure silver coins, that have lain at the bottom of the sea for 250 years. Like most serious divers, we've laughed at stories of sunken treasure; but we don't laugh any more.

Soon we'll be going back to this wreck, equipped for more that photography. We don't know how much we'll be able to salvage . . . but at least I know what my next book will be about.

Colombo, April 1961.

3 GREAT SCIENCE FICTION CLASSICS FOR ONLY $1

CHILDHOOD'S END   by Arthur C. Clarke

The most famous book of this distinguished author-scientist. Written with intellectual daring and vaulting imagination, it tells of a world made perfect and a race transformed—and of the unexpected tragedy of perfection.

MORE THAN HUMAN   by Theodore Sturgeon

Winner of the International Fantasy Award, this is the story of how six people met, and what they became—together. An unforgettable "classic" of Gestalt theory, MORE THAN HUMAN is Sturgeon at his brilliant, provocative best.

SOMETIME, NEVER   by William Golding, John Wyndham and Mervyn Peake

Three outstanding short novels in one book—winner of a Special Award from "If" Magazine. "What a really off-beat collection! There's not a humdrum idea in the book . . ."
—Groff Conklin

Other Ballantine Science Fiction . . . .